THE HA... CONQUEST OF SPACE

by

BRUCE L. CATHIE

1994/5
Nexus Magazine

MW01006784

Copyright © 1994, 1995, Bruce L. Cathie
All rights reserved

First Edition, 1995

No part of this publication may be reproduced or transmitted in any form
or by any means, electronic or mechanical, including photocopy, recording, or any information storage and retrieval system now known or to be
invented, without permission in writing from the publisher, except by a
reviewer who wishes to quote brief passages in connection with a review
written for inclusion in a magazine, newspaper or broadcast.

National Library of Australia Cataloguing - in - Publication entry

Cathie, Bruce L.
The Harmonic Conquest Of Space
Includes Index

ISBN 0 646 21679 1

Cover image by Human Touch/The Image Bank, Sydney, Australia

NEXUS Magazine
PO Box 30
Mapleton, Queensland, 4560
Australia
Tel: 074 42 9280 (International +61 74 42 9280)
Fax: 074 42 9381   (International +61 74 42 9381)

Printed and bound in Australia

CONTENTS

LIST OF DIAGRAMS

LIST OF TABLES

LIST OF MAPS

LIST OF PHOTOCOPIES

ACKNOWLEDGEMENTS

Abel, Morrison and Wolf, *Exploration of the Universe*, Saunders College Publishing, New York, NY, United States of America, 1987.

Robert G. Adams, Inventor of the Adams Pulsed Electric Motor Generator, Whakatane, New Zealand.

Michael Baigent, Richard Leigh, Henry Lincoln, *The Holy Blood and The Holy Grail*, Transworld Publishers Ltd, London, United Kingdom, 1983.

Halliday & Resnick, *Physics*, John Wiley & Sons Inc., NY, USA, 1960.

Clive Harold, *The Uninvited*, W. H. Allen & Co. Ltd, London, UK, 1979.

Stephen Hawking, *Beyond the Black Hole*, William Collins Sons & Co. Ltd, Glasgow, UK, 1985.

Richard C. Hoagland, *Analysis of the Pyramid on Mars*, The Mars Mission, NJ, USA.

Larousse, *Astronomy*, The Hamlyn Publishing Group Ltd, Twickenham, Middlesex, UK, 1987.

Henry Lincoln, *The Holy Place*, Transworld Publishers Ltd, London, UK, 1992.

John Michell, *City of Revelation*, Garnstone Press Ltd, London, UK, 1972.

Dr Hans A. Nieper, *Revolution in Technology, Medicine and Society*, Druckhaus Neue Stalling, Oldenburg, Germany, 1985.

Frank Scully, *Behind the Flying Saucers*, Victor Gollancz Ltd, London, UK, 1950.

The Edgar Cayce Foundation, PO Box 595, Virginia Beach, Virginia 23451, United States of America.

The New Zealand Herald, Auckland, New Zealand.

The New Zealand Listener, Wellington, New Zealand.

The Star, Auckland, New Zealand.

Time, Time, Inc., Chicago, Illinois, USA.

Colin Wilson, *Beyond the Occult*, Bantam Press, London, UK, 1988.

David Wood, *Genisis*, The Baton Press, Tunbridge Wells, Kent, UK, 1985.

A special thank-you to Mr Rodney Maupin (1211 144th Street S.E., Mill Creek, Washington 981012, USA). Rodney has spent countless hours compiling all the mathematical information into a computer program that can now be used for research into the harmonics of the Earth's energy system. We now work together to computerise all the data as it is discovered. (See information regarding the *Gridworks* program at the back of this book.)

DEFINITIONS OF TERMS

Harmony and harmonic, as defined by the *Britannica World Standard Dictionary*:

1. Harmony: a state of order, agreement or completeness in the relations of things of parts of a whole to each other.

2. Harmonic: producing, characterised by or pertaining to harmony.

a. Music: pertaining to a tone whose rate of vibration is an exact multiple of a given primary tone.

b. Mathematical: derived from or originally suggested by the numerical relations between the vibrations of the musical harmonies or overtones of the same fundamental tone; harmonic functions.

c. Physics: any component of a periodic quantity which is an integral multiple of the fundamental frequency.

In this book, I discuss the fundamental harmonies of the vibrational frequencies which form the building blocks of our immediate Universe and those of the theoretical anti-Universe, which modern scientists have postulated as existing in mirror-like image of our own. I theorise that the whole of physical reality which is tangible to us is formed from the basic geometric harmonies or harmonics of the angular velocities, or waveforms, of light. From these basic harmonies or resonating wave-forms, myriad other waves are created which blend in sympathetic resonance, one with the other, thus forming the physical structures. Reality, in essence, is similar to a hologram.

Einstein stated that the geometric structure of space-time determines the physical processes. I theorise that space and time manifest from the geometric harmonies of the wave-motions of light—the maximum fundamental harmonic of light, in geometric terms, being an angular velocity of 144,000 minutes of arc or nautical miles per grid second in relation to the Earth's surface and there being 97,000 grid seconds to one revolution of the Earth.

It follows that the 'speed' of light, and time, would be directly related to one minute of arc on the surface of any other spherical planetary body. The 'speed' of light, in fact, is not a constant. It depends on the observer's relative position in space.

Introduction

The events which led up to the writing of this, my fifth book, began in 1952 when my life changed dramatically. I was then a pilot with the New Zealand National Airways Corporation, and one evening, with a group of friends, I had a prolonged sighting of a UFO over the Manukau Harbour in Auckland, New Zealand.

The object carried out manoeuvres that no known man-made vehicle could accomplish at that time. The thing, whatever it was, had an intensely brilliant white light with a smaller glowing red light some distance from it, and for about twenty minutes held me and the other witnesses spellbound as it went through a series of right-angle turns, then disappeared into a clear evening sky.

Ever since then I have collected every bit of information available on the UFO phenomenon. During my thousands of hours of flying, I searched the skies constantly and have been rewarded with many other sightings. As time went on, I was informed by other airline pilots in New Zealand that they, too, were sighting objects for which they could find no explanation. It became very obvious that either we were being observed by some sort of advanced vehicles coming in from outer space—or that some scientific group on Earth had discovered a principle of physics unknown to the rest of us, and secret research of some nature was being carried out. I am now sure that both views are correct and that much is being kept from the public.

Over the years I have studied a great deal of material published by other investigating groups, and came to the conclusion that no real progress could be made in discovering the purpose of UFO activity by this means. The main body of investigators seem to have confined their activity to collecting masses of sighting reports, filing them away and then doing nothing else with the information. Very little practical use has been made with any of it.

I decided long ago that the only way to tackle the problem would be to plot all the areas of activity and try to find some logical mathematical order in the hovering positions or flight paths of the unknowns. To this purpose, I studied the methods of a Frenchman by the name of Aimé Michel who had also endeavoured to find a mathematical order of this nature. He had had partial success and managed to find several tracklines with equally spaced activity in the European area. Just when he appeared to be onto something, for some unknown reason he abandoned this line of research and publicly proclaimed that nothing could be accomplished by this method. After studying his earlier attempts, I considered that there was definite logic in his findings and decided that I would carry on my own research using his basic methods.

I struck gold, and ever since I plotted the first two tracklines at right angles in the New Zealand area I have continued to progress and advance my scientific knowledge in areas which otherwise would normally be completely foreign to me.

Along the way I have taken much flack from the academic world and from those who profess to know all the answers—that is, in public. But behind the scenes it has been a different story. Over the years I have had many direct communications from members of intelligence organisations, top scientific circles and government agencies, wishing to know what my latest findings were and requesting copies of certain parts of my work.

Once I had established the two tracklines, I was able to form a complete grid network over the whole of the New Zealand area by gradually plotting into the survey map the most reliable UFO sightings. The pattern consisted of lines spaced at thirty-minute intervals oriented just on six degrees displacement from true north. Eventually, two similar grids were found to be interlocked with each other, creating rather a complex pattern which could be further reduced to lines with a spacing of seven-and-one-half minutes. I have made use of this map for many years and still find the grid lines valid when checking recent activity.

The next logical conclusion was that I had discovered a small section of what could possibly be a world system. The question was how to transfer this small section onto the world sphere and accurately align it. It was then brought to my notice that a strange aerial-like object had been photographed by chance on the seabed off the west coast of South America by the American survey ship *Eltanin*. The object was two to three feet high and had six main crossbars spaced evenly up its stem, with a smaller one on top. Each set of crossbars had a small ball at the end of each arm. A friend and I visited the *Eltanin* when it came into the Port of Auckland and we were told by one of the scientists on board that the object was thought to be an artefact of some kind and appeared to be metallic.

I had a hunch that this could be the point I was looking for upon which to orientate a world grid, if in fact one existed. I spent some time constructing grid patterns on a plastic ball until I found a system which could be transferred onto the world surface and aligned with the aerial-type object and the section of the grid discovered over New Zealand. I found that the patterns matched and felt sure then that a global system was almost a certainty.

The next step was to find the mathematical basis of the system, and this proved to be a long and arduous job—especially as I do not class myself as anything of a mathematician or a physicist. After a study of all the available information on UFO activity, I came to the conclusion that the speed of light, mass and gravity acceleration values must have some connection with the grid structure in order to explain the extraordinary manoeuvres carried out by the strange craft.

The basic grid structure was formed by a series of great circles interlocking at various points around the Earth's surface. The nodal points of the two grids, when joined by a series of small and great circles, formed what I have loosely termed 'polar squares' around the north and south geographic poles. It was when I carried out a geometric and mathematical analysis of these sections that I found a direct connection with light, gravity and mass equivalents, in a harmonic sense. To do this I had to convert all our normal systems of measurement into a single set of units and also convert our time measure into one that would correlate with the grid. After much thought and a long period of trial and error I finally found that angular measure in minute-of-arc values, and a time unit based on twenty-seven units for one revolution of the Earth, was the key to unlocking the grid secrets.

After that, it was a long and slow process to learn how to relate the values being calculated, one to the other, in order to find a logical mathematical basis for the system.

Finally, after years of work, I discovered that I could formulate a series of harmonic unified equations which indicated that the whole of physical reality was in fact manifested by a complex pattern of interlocking wave-forms. I gradually found that the harmonic values could be applied to all branches of scientific research and atomic theory. At first I was not very sure of the results I was getting but, as time went by, more and more interest was being shown by intelligence agents, government personnel and scientists in the work that I was doing, and many requests started coming in for information. Help in my work was eventually offered from these quarters but the catch was that I had to remain silent about my discoveries. This I refused to do, and still continue to battle along on my own. Once I realised the importance of the material in my possession I considered it extremely dangerous for any small group of people to have complete control of it.

It was only a matter of time before I realised that the energy network formed by the grid was already known to a powerful group of international interests and scientists. It became obvious that the system had many military applications and that political advantage could be obtained by those with secret knowledge of this nature. With this knowledge, it would be possible for a comparatively small group to take over control of the world. I have continually asked these people for a valid moral reason why the information should not be given to the world community, and so far no answer has been given—so I carry on publishing the material as I find it.

One of the most startling facts that I discovered by the application of grid mathematics was that an atomic bomb is a device based on the geometrics of space and time. To be successfully detonated, the bomb must be geometrically constructed, placed on, under or over a geometric position in relation to the Earth's surface, and activated at a specific time in relation to the geometrics of the solar system. I found that it was possible to precalculate the times of various bomb tests and the locations where it was possible to explode a bomb. When it became known that I had discovered this well-kept secret, I was offered a position by the American Central Intelligence Agency.

The offer was very tempting but I decided that I could not sign my freedom away, and after two days I turned it down. According to the mathematical complexities of unlocking the geometric structure of the unstable material constituting a bomb in order to create a sudden release of energy, I realised that an all-out atomic war was an impossibility: both sides could precalculate well in advance the time and positions of atomic attack; plus the fact that only certain geometric locations could be devastated anyhow. This could be the reason for the proliferation of conventional weapons in modern warfare. Now, of course, the Russians and the Americans are in the process of dismantling the atomic warfare machine and beginning to cooperate in more peaceful ventures. The atomic threat has served its political purpose.

Another application of the grid unified harmonics is the production of energy. With the right know-how and with comparatively simple apparatus similar to a radio receiver, an unlimited amount of free electrical energy can be tapped from the gravitational fields inherent in the energy system. This has already been done in the past by one of the greatest technical geniuses in history, Dr Nikola Tesla. Dr T. Henry Moray also invented apparatus that would tap gravitational energy directly.

It is said that Dr Tesla constructed a car which had an electric motor that derived its energy directly from the surrounding gravitational field. The car could reach speeds around 90 miles per hour. I would advise readers to gather all the information they can on the attainments of these two men. Their work obviously has been suppressed.

"It is not right for the public to have this knowledge," I was told by one of my contacts who worked for an intelligence organisation. "It would not be good for them," he said. I am sure that most of you would disagree with this outlook. It is up to the scientific community itself to open up research in all these fields in order that all mankind can reap the benefits.

In the early years of my research I believed that the grid system had been set up artificially by the geometric placement of specialised electromagnetic transmitters. As time went on I realised that this was not correct. The grid system is formed naturally by the electromagnetic fields of the Earth itself. In theory, all spherical bodies in the Universe are formed the same way. The electronic hardware that I had discovered in my research was gear that had been built into the natural system. The scientists know about it and are tapping into it.

I am still progressing in my research into the world energy system and the geometric nature of the Universe. During the last few years I have managed to compile all the discovered harmonic unified values into a set of unified tables which can now be used for research in many areas of scientific interest. I discovered that I could convert the gravitational acceleration values in the physics books into geometric values, and correlate them directly with the harmonic geometrics derived from the grid system.

After all these years, the latest computer tables indicate that the geometric harmonic of 695, published in my earlier works, is in fact a direct conversion of gravity acceleration. The tables show quite clearly that the harmonic of gravity acceleration is the reciprocal of the harmonic of the acceleration, or deceleration, of light. The term 'speed' of light is a misnomer. The confusion is caused by the relative motions involved in the calculations.

The Universe is now open to us.

We can reach any part of it by means of the harmonic conquest of space.

Chapter One

MATHEMATICS OF THE WORLD GRID

UPDATED 1994

The information in this chapter regarding the structure and mathematical values built into the system consists of material condensed from my first four books, plus the findings derived from my recent research up to early 1993. Over the last few years I have had the use of computers and, recently, special programs that have helped me to increase the accuracy of my research and assemble the mathematical values into a much more understandable order.

In a general way I was convinced that UFOs were actively engaged in a survey of the Earth for some definite reason. I felt that their visits were not haphazard—they were not just on casual sightseeing tours. Quite a number of investigators around the world had come to the conclusion that the sightings were beginning to form a pattern. At this period, however, the pattern was so complex as to defy any definition or solution. By the correlation of sightings, small sections of track had been identified and some UFOs had been observed moving along these set paths. Some of these had hovered over certain spots at set intervals, but these bits and pieces of tracklines were so scattered around the surface of our planet that it was quite impossible to fit them together into any semblance of order.

I was certain that if an overall pattern could be found and plotted, it might be possible to establish the reason behind UFO activity. I considered that the pattern would be geometric if these things were intelligently controlled, and that if somehow I could find the key to one section then I might solve the rest by duplication and inference.

I had sighted a number of unidentified objects in the sky over a period of several years, and by correlating two of these with other data I was eventually able to construct a grid system which covered the whole world.

One of these sightings was in 1956. I was a DC3 co-pilot crewing a flight from Auckland to Paraparaumu. It was about 6 pm, conditions were calm and there was unlimited visibility. We were just south of Waverley at 7,000 feet when I saw this object at an extremely high altitude in the east. I drew the captain's attention to it and together we watched it travel in a curved trajectory from east to west across our track until it disappeared in a flash of light at about 10,000 feet in the area of D'Urville Island. It appeared to travel across New Zealand in the vicinity or slightly to the north of Cook Strait, and it was so large that two streaks, similar to vapour trails, were seen to extend from either side of its pale green disc.

When about halfway across the strait, a small object detached itself from the parent body and dropped vertically until it disappeared. It looked almost as if the main disc was at such a high temperature that a globule had dripped from it. I thought about this later and decided that if that were so, the small object would also have a curved trajectory in the direction of the parent body. But this was not so; it detached and dropped 'vertically' down at great speed. There could be only one answer for this action: the small body must have been controlled.

Calculations at a later date proved this UFO to have been between 1,500 and 2,000 feet in diameter. A report in a Nelson newspaper the following day described an explosion at a high altitude to the north of the city. The shock wave broke windows in some local glasshouses.

My other sighting occurred on 12th March 1965. This was the best and most interesting of them all, and from then on my investigations proceeded with all speed until they culminated in my present findings.

I had always expected to see UFOs in the sky and that was where my attention was usually focussed. While flying, I was always ready and alert to analyse any object sighted from the aircraft. I never expected to find a UFO landing at my feet and, so far, this has never happened. This sighting, however, was different from all the others because I observed it lying under about thirty feet of water.

I was scheduled to carry out a positioning flight from Whenuapai, Auckland's main airport at the time, to Kaitaia, at the northern tip of New Zealand. Departure was at 11 am, and as there were no passengers involved and the weather was perfect I decided to fly visually to

Kaitaia along the west coast. An officer from the operations department was on board, and this was a good opportunity to show him some of the rugged country to the north. (I must stress that air traffic regulations were strictly observed during the flight.)

On leaving Whenuapai I climbed to clear the area, and when approaching the southern end of the Kaipara Harbour, just north of Helensville, I dropped to a lower altitude to have a better look at anything in the flight path. The tide in the harbour was well out and the water over the mud-flats and estuaries was quite shallow.

We were about a third of the way across the harbour when I spotted what I took to be a stranded grey-white whale. I veered slightly to port, to fly more directly over the object and to obtain a better look.

I suppose a pilot develops a habit of keeping his emotions to himself. As far as I can remember, I gave no indication of surprise and I said nothing as I looked down. My 'whale' was definitely a metal fish. I could see it very clearly, and I quote from the notes I made later:

(a) The object was perfectly streamlined and symmetrical in shape.

(b) It had no external control surfaces or protrusions.

(c) It appeared metallic and there was a suggestion of a hatch on top, streamlined in shape. It was not quite halfway along the body as measured from the nose.

(d) It was resting on the bottom of the estuary and headed towards the south, as suggested from the streamlined shape.

(e) The shape was not that of a normal submarine and there was no superstructure.

(f) I estimated the length as 100 feet, with a diameter of 15 feet at the widest part.

(g) The object rested in no more than 30 feet of clear water. The bottom of the harbour was visible and the craft was sharply defined.

Enquiries made with the Navy confirmed that it would not have been possible for a normal submarine to be in this particular position due to the configuration of the harbour and coastline.

An American engineer checked this spot on the harbour with a depth-sounder in September 1969. He informed me afterwards that a hole had been detected in the harbour bed approximately one-eighth-of-a-mile wide and over 100 feet deep, which I consider would indicate some activity had been carried out in this position at some previous time. I published this report in my second book. More about this man in a later chapter.

I had a further key to the puzzle in April 1965. My wife saw an

advertisement in the local paper seeking members for a UFO organisation called the New Zealand Scientific and Space Research
Organisation. I contacted this organisation and found that a vast
amount of information had been very efficiently compiled. Material
had been collected from twenty-five different countries over a period of
twelve years. I was invited to study the information at leisure.

Amongst this mass of data I discovered the reports of a UFO that had
been seen from several different localities in both islands of New
Zealand on 26th March 1965. People in Napier, New Plymouth,
Palmerston North, Wanganui, Fielding and Otaki Forks in the north
islands, and Nelson coast road, Blenheim and Westport (Cape
Foulwind) in the south island, had all reported sightings.

It was decided that I try to plot the track of this UFO. From the considerable amount of information available, I found that the maximum
variation in times of sightings from all areas was 15 minutes. Most
reports gave the time as 9.45 pm. This proved that the object must
have been very large and at a high altitude during the greater part of its
trajectory.

There was nothing of any great significance or originality in these
accounts and they followed the pattern of many other sightings.
However, from the mass of detail supplied by so many different people
over so wide an area, it was possible to plot the track of the object with
reasonable accuracy. I started work on a Mercator's plotting chart, and
after several hours of checking one report against the other and calculating possible elevations and trajectories, I felt I had refined the plot
sufficiently to draw in the final track of the object. The result is shown
on Map 1.

The track began about seventy nautical miles north of New
Plymouth, passed just over to the west of Mt Egmont and finished at
D'Urville Island. When first seen, the altitude would have been about
30,000 feet curving down on a flight path to somewhere around 10,000
feet when it disappeared.

Some time after those sightings on 26th March 1965, I had another
look at the plot I had made. I could find no flaws in my thinking but I
needed more information. As I was to discover many times later, the
clues were quite obvious, but I was not then sufficiently expert in real-
ising their significance. In point of fact, this first trackline was to be
the starting point of a whole string of discoveries of which I have yet to
find an end.

I pored over that plot for a long time before it suddenly occurred to

Map 1

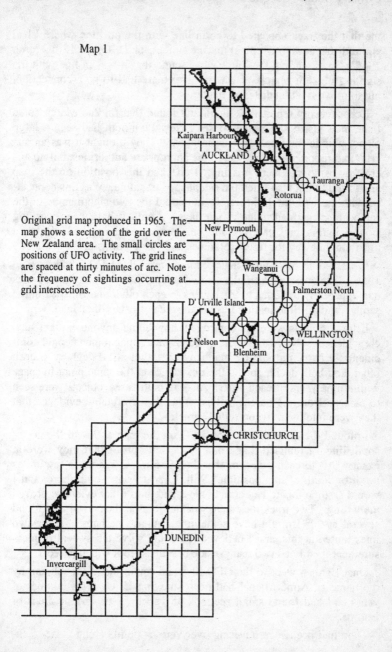

Original grid map produced in 1965. The map shows a section of the grid over the New Zealand area. The small circles are positions of UFO activity. The grid lines are spaced at thirty minutes of arc. Note the frequency of sightings occurring at grid intersections.

me that the track appeared to be in line with the position where I had sighted the unidentified submarine object, or USO, on 12th March 1965. On extending the line back, I found that it was in line with the sighting of 26th March. I was positive there had to be a connection, but to prove it was a different matter.

I checked my report files again and found that on 2nd March some fishermen just north of the coast of New Plymouth had seen a large object plunge into the sea and disappear. They thought it was an aircraft and reported the incident to the appropriate authorities, but no aircraft or personnel were missing. I checked this position on the map and found that it also fitted the established trackline. Was this connected with the USO of 12th March, and could the two sightings be of the same object sighted twice in ten days? Could it have been working slowly up this track carrying out some project on the seabed? I tucked this thought away for future reference and carried on with the search.

It was some days later that I remembered the UFO I had seen in 1956. This object was similar and, most significant of all, both objects had apparently travelled at 90 degrees to each other and finished in the same grand all-illuminating flash in the area of D'Urville Island.

If these objects were not controlled, how could anyone explain such coincidences? No two meteors or other natural phenomena could coincidentally carry out similar manoeuvres, travel at 90 degrees to each other, and both decide to end their existence at the same point in space within nine years of each other. Also, in both cases, objects were seen to emerge from the parent bodies. Was this irrefutable evidence that they were intelligently controlled vehicles?

I plotted the track of the 1956 UFO on the map at 90° to the north-south line. I realised that I had no definite proof that they were at exactly 90° to each other, or that the 1956 track was not a few miles north or south of this position. Still, I had to start somewhere, and I would assume this to be correct unless and until other evidence proved me wrong. Two tracklines at 90° meant little on their own. If I found several at 90° I might have something. A grid perhaps? These two lines hinted at this, and I believed if I could solve the system of measurement then I had two ready-made baselines from which to work.

Once again I went to the UFO files and found that a Frenchman by the name of Aimé Michel had been studying UFOs for a number of years and had found small sections of tracklines in various areas of Europe.

They had been seen hovering over various points along these tracklines, and Mr Michel had observed that the average distance between these points was 54.43 kilometres. By itself this was only a small grain of information but, like a starting gun, it set me off again.

Using the Kaipara Harbour as a starting point, I marked off the 54.43-kilometre intervals along the trackline I had found. I was disappointed when I was unsuccessful in obtaining an even distribution of positions to the D'Urville Island disappearing point. I checked and rechecked but nothing worked out. I slept on the problem and next day I had the answer.

I remembered that a great number of sightings had occurred around the Blenheim area. Even before the advent of ordinary aircraft in New Zealand, this area had been visited by UFOs. I had read about them in old copies of the local papers, and many recent sightings suggested again that this area had something special about it.

So I dragged out my map and extended the trackline until it cut a 90° coordinate from the town of Blenheim. The distance from this point to the Kaipara position I found to be exactly 300 nautical miles, and one nautical mile is equal to one minute of arc on the Earth's surface. Could it be that the rough interval 54.43 kilometres discovered by Michel was, in fact, an interval of 30 nautical miles when corrected? If so, then this interval could be evenly spaced along my trackline ten times. Was this the system of measurement used by the UFOs? There was no proof of course but it seemed a reasonable assumption. A minute of arc is a measurement which could be applied to the whole Universe.

University personnel and others in the academic field attacked me repeatedly over this issue. They maintained that degrees and minutes of arc were arbitrary values set up by the ancient mathematicians and that therefore my calculations were meaningless. I finally found proof of my argument in the works of Pythagoras. As my research progressed, I discovered that the harmonic of the speed of light in free space had a value of 144. If this was divided by 2 to find the harmonic of one half-cycle or half-wave, the answer was 72. If this value was then applied to the Pythagoras right-angled 3,4,5 triangle, and each side was extended in this ratio, then the figure had sides of 216, 288 and 360 units. The harmonic proportions thus derived were equal to:

216 = 21600 = the number of minutes of arc in a circle
360 = 360 = the number of degrees in a circle
288 = (144 x 2) = 2c, where 'c' = the speed-of-light harmonic

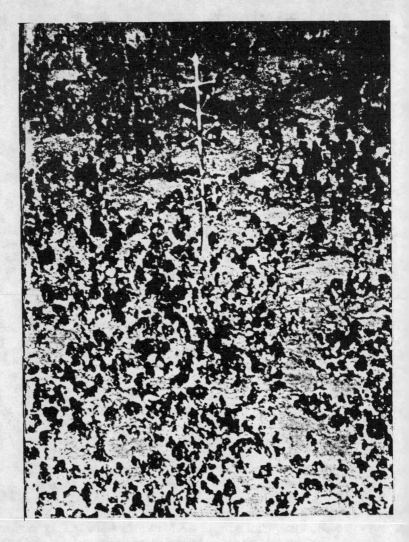

Photocopy 1
Eltanin Aerial

It appeared from this that the harmonic of light had a very definite relationship with the geometry of a circle and that the early mathematicians were fully aware of the fact. This will become clearer as you read through this book.

The fifth interval of 30 nautical miles from the Kaipara position coincided with the position off the coast of New Plymouth where the mysterious object had plunged into the sea. The plotted points of disappearance of the two large UFOs in the D'Urville Island area did not quite match up with the ninth interval, but this did not worry me unduly as I expected that a small percentage of error must be inherent in my original plot. I readjusted this position to the ninth interval and carried on the search to see how many other sightings I could fit into this pattern.

The results exceeded my expectations. I found that by using units of 30 minutes of arc latitude north-south and 30 minutes of arc longitude east-west on my Mercator's map, a grid pattern was formed into which a great number of UFO reports could be fitted. I eventually had a map with sixteen stationary and seventeen moving UFOs plotted on grid intersections and tracklines.

Having satisfied myself that my reasoning and plotting were not false, I considered that I had good proof that New Zealand, possibly other countries and probably the whole world were being systematically covered by some type of grid system.

I subsequently discovered that the grid lattice could be further divided. It is now evident that the grid lines in the main system are spaced at intervals of 7.5 minutes of arc, north-south and east-west. The importance of this will prove itself when compared with the rest of the calculations in this book. There are 21,600 minutes of arc in a circle, and when this is divided by 7.5 we get a value of 2880. The grid lattice is therefore tuned harmonically to twice the speed of light (288), as will be shown in other sections.

It appeared that I had found a section of geometric grid pattern in the New Zealand area. I now had to form some theory of construction for the whole world. I could then possibly fit the New Zealand section into it. By drawing a series of patterns on a small plastic ball, I finally found a system that could be used as a starting point for a global investigation. The basic pattern is shown in Diagram 1.

I was sure I was on the right track, but now I had to superimpose this pattern on the world globe. It was essential that I find a point position somewhere on the Earth upon which to orientate the geometric pattern.

Diagram 1

Showing the relationship of a grid polar square to the geographic pole.
Each grid has a similar pattern. The pole of each grid is set at a different
latitude and longitude.

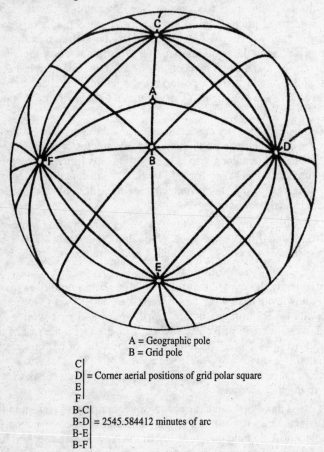

A = Geographic pole
B = Grid pole

$\left.\begin{array}{l}C \\ D \\ E \\ F\end{array}\right|$ = Corner aerial positions of grid polar square

$\left.\begin{array}{l}B-C \\ B-D \\ B-E \\ B-F\end{array}\right|$ = 2545.584412 minutes of arc

The displacement (A - B) has a different value for each grid.

(A - B) Grid "A"   = 1054.255313 minutes of arc
(A - B) Grid "B"   =   694.8832574 minutes of arc
(A - B) Grid "C"   =   867.6871800 minutes of arc

I finally came up with an item of news that gave me a very important clue on how to proceed.

On 29th August 1964 the American survey ship *Eltanin* was carrying out a sweep of the seabed off the coast of South America. A series of submarine photographs was being taken of the area by means of a camera attached to a long cable. A surprise was in store when these photographs were developed. On one of the prints, in marvellous detail, was an aerial-type object sticking up from an otherwise featureless seabed.

This object appeared to be metallic and perfectly symmetrical in construction. The array consisted of six main crossbars with small knob-like ends and a small crossbar at the top. Each cross looked to be set at an angle of 15 degrees to the others, and the whole system stood about two feet in height. The position where this object was found was given as latitude 59° 08' south, longitude 105° west.

As this bit of ironmongery was situated at a depth of 13,500 feet below the surface, I was certain that no human engineers had placed it there.

Scientists may be able to descend to those depths in specially constructed bathyspheres, but I don't think they could work as deeply as that on a precision engineering problem. In view of my earlier sightings in the Kaipara Harbour, I was willing to accept that the aerial-type object had been placed there by an unidentified submarine object, or USO.

Since this photo was taken, there has been a determined attempt by the scientific world to label this object as nothing more than a plant of some sort. A journalist friend and I managed to visit the *Eltanin* during one of its few visits to New Zealand, and when we discussed this object with some of the scientists on board, the comment was that it was classed as an artefact. This was before the great hush-up, but regardless of that I believe that the mathematical proofs will show without doubt that the object is artificial and most probably an aerial of some sort.

The form of this aerial-like structure also fitted in with the general pattern of the grid as I had envisaged it on the plastic ball. The six main crossbars denoted the radiating points of six, or twelve, great circles which form the main structure of the grid.

I centred the grid on the position of the object found by the *Eltanin,* and the 180° reciprocal of this in Russian Siberia, lining the whole thing up with the section I had found in New Zealand. I found the system to be lined up very closely with the magnetic field of the Earth. The equator of the grid followed very closely the line of zero dip around the world (that is, the positions on the Earth's surface where a magnetic compass needle has only a horizontal and no vertical component).

In my first two books I discussed the methods I used to line up the system and calculate the first estimates of the grid pole positions and the major focal points of the grid similar to the *Eltanin* 'aerial' placement.

In this earlier work I placed the reciprocal position of the *Eltanin* 'aerial' at a latitude of 59° 08' north and longitude 75° east. Recent computer analysis would now place the aerial at a position of 59° 09' 17.93" north and 75° 00' 36" east. This would, of course, mean that the original position given in the local newspaper for the *Eltanin* aerial, of 59° 08' south and 105° west, was in error. All present indications on the computer give a true position of latitude 59° 09' 17.93" south and longitude 104° 59' 24" west. The equivalent position on energy grid "B" would then be latitude 47.573593326° south and longitude 0.00°, or grid longitude zero and 2545.5844 minutes of arc from Grid Pole "B" in the south.

At the time, when the survey ship was in the Port of Auckland, the scientists probably passed a rough position along with a copy of the photograph to the local newspaper. It is possible that they did not want the exact position to be known. They now try to pass the object off as some type of plant life.

I calculated the length of the diagonal of what I call for simplicity the 'polar grid square' and found it to be 5091.168825 minutes of arc long. I plotted a track from the Siberian position through the north geographic pole and measured off this distance to locate another corner 'aerial' of the polar square.

'Square' is not technically the right word to use, as the four sides are formed by sections of small circles which are in different planes to each other. When the 'polar square' areas are transferred from the surface of the Earth sphere onto a flat plane such as a map, then a perfect square is formed with sides 3600 minutes long and diagonals 5091.168825 minutes of arc.

Once I had established this first baseline, I found it quite easy to construct the main skeleton of the grid over the whole surface of the Earth.

Soon I found that there were in fact two similar grids interlocked with each other. The poles of the grids were spaced at different distances from the geographic poles, and this arrangement set up a series of geometric harmonics which were directly related to the speed of light, mass and gravity. The interaction of the two grids created a harmonic resonance which, in turn, formed a third resultant grid.

The theoretical positions for Grid Poles "A", "B" and "C" in the northern hemisphere are as follows:

Grid Pole "A":	Latitude:	72° 25' 44.6812" north
	Longitude:	89° 58' 59.4336" west
Grid Pole "B":	Latitude:	78° 25' 07.0046" north
	Longitude:	104° 59' 24" west
Grid Pole "C":	Latitude:	75° 32' 18.7692" north
	Longitude:	95° 58' 07.1695" west

The poles will be in reciprocal positions in the southern hemisphere.

The diagonal of the 'polar square' of 5091.168825 units can be broken down into a series of values:

5091.168825 ÷ 2	= 2545.584412
Reciprocal of 2545.584412	= 0.039283710
Square of 2545.584412	= 648

The harmonic value of 3928371 is of extreme importance as it has a direct relationship with the Earth's magnetic field. The harmonic 648 also has many interesting associations—in particular, the harmonic table for temperature.

I have been able to check activity in other parts of the world by applying harmonic calculation to certain positions of latitude and longitude. It is not necessary to use the grid structure to carry out some types of calculation once the harmonic process is understood.

In my second book (*Harmonic 695: The UFO and Anti-Gravity*), I stated that the first glimmerings of how true space travel might be achieved came to me when I uncovered the clues that led me to the UFO grid that criss-crosses the globe.

I was aware that my calculations were not precisely accurate in the strict mathematical sense but I could see that the system was based on space-time geometrics, and there was the best possible support for this from no less than the theories of Albert Einstein.

Somewhere, I knew, the system contained a clue to the truth of the unified field which he had postulated permeates all of existence. I did not know at the time that this knowledge was already in the hands of scientists who were well ahead of me. I know now that they must have been aware of the grid system for many years. They knew that Einstein's ideas about the unified field were correct and, what's more, they have been carrying out full-scale research into the practical applications of the mathematical concepts contained in that theory.

We were told that Einstein died without completing his equations relating to the unified theory. But in more recent times it has been said that he did in fact complete his work and that the concepts were so advanced that the full truth was not released.

The only way to traverse the vast distances of space is to possess the means of manipulating or altering the very structure of space itself—altering the space-time geometric matrix, which to us provides the illusion of form and distance. The method of achieving this lies in the alteration of the frequencies controlling the matter-antimatter cycles that govern our awareness or perception of position in the space-time structure. Time itself is a geometric, just as Einstein postulated. If time can be altered, then the whole Universe is accessible to us. We are now on the threshold of exploring deep space.

In the blink of an eye we could cross immense distances, for distance is but an illusion. The only thing that keeps places apart in space is time. If it were possible to move from one position to another in space in an infinitely small amount of time, or zero time, then both the positions would coexist according to our awareness. By speeding up the geometric of time, we will be able to bring distant places within close proximity. This is the secret of the UFOs. They travel by means of altering the spatial dimensions around them and repositioning in space-time.

I decided to concentrate specifically on three harmonic values which appeared to have a close relationship with each other. Previously I had shown this connection and had truthfully pointed out that I did not know why the relationship was there at all.

At the time I did not have computers to work with, and the values calculated were only very rough estimates of those presently available. The harmonic values which occupied my full attention were:

1703: This was a four-figure harmonic of 170,300,000,000 which was the expression in cubic minutes of arc, or nautical miles, of the mass or volume of planet Earth and its surrounding atmosphere.

1439: A four-figure harmonic of 143,900 minutes of arc or nautical miles per grid second, representing the then known speed of light in grid values.

2640: This figure, expressed in minutes of arc or nautical miles, was built into the polar portion of the grid structure as a geometric coordinate when the curved pattern was transferred onto a flat plane.

I found that when I matched these values harmonically, the results were as follows (zeros to the right-hand side can be ignored in this form of harmonic calculation):

$$
\begin{array}{r}
1703 \\
- 264 \\
\hline
1439
\end{array}
$$

In other words, the difference between the harmonic of mass and the harmonic of light was the harmonic of 264 (or 2640). It was apparent that if my calculations were more accurate it should be possible to find out just what the 2640 figure referred to. After more calculation, the following terms were found:

17025	Earth mass harmonic
- 2636	unknown harmonic
14389	speed-of-light harmonic

Checking through some five-figure mathematical tables, I found to my surprise that 2.6363 is the square root of 6.95 (from the 1-10 square root tables). In harmonic calculation, decimal points as well as zeros to the right or left of the figure can be ignored; so it could be said that the square root of the harmonic 695 was the harmonic 2636. I could perceive from this the first steps necessary to solve the elusive equation. I had established that 695 was the harmonic reciprocal of the speed of light, or 1/1439, subject to the accuracy of my calculations at the time.

It was now possible to substitute algebraic values, although obviously a computer would be necessary to solve the true values to extreme accuracy.

17025	Earth mass
- 2636	the square root of the speed-of-light reciprocal
14389	the speed of light

Therefore, if   c = the speed of light

                m = mass

Then $m = [c + \sqrt{(1/c)}]$

I had the first part of a unified field equation in harmonic values. To take the next step I first had to go back to Einsteinian theory, particularly the famous equation $E = mc^2$, where 'E' = energy, 'm' = mass, and 'c' = the speed of light.

Einstein declared that physical matter was nothing more than a concentrated field of force. What we term a physical substance is, in reality, an intangible concentration of wave-forms. Different concentrations of structural patterns of waves unite to form the myriad chemicals and elements which in turn react with one another to form physical substances. Different wave-forms of matter appear to us to be solid because we are constituted of similar wave-forms which resonate within a clearly defined range of frequencies that control the physical processes of our limited world.

Einstein believed that 'm', the value for mass in the equation, could eventually be removed and a value substituted that would express the physical in the form of pure energy. In other words, by substituting for 'm', a unified field equation should result which would express in mathematical terms the whole of existence including this Universe and everything within it.

Einstein maintained that the 'm' in his equation could be replaced by a term denoting wave-form. I had found a substitute for 'm' in terms of wave-forms of light. So the obvious step to me was to replace Einstein's 'm' with the values of 'c' found from the grid system. The results are as follows:

Einstein: $E = mc^2$

Cathie Grid: $m = [c + \sqrt{(1/c)}]$

Therefore, $E = [c + \sqrt{(1/c)(c)^2}]$ — **Harmonic Equation 1**

I NOW HAD A HARMONIC UNIFIED FIELD EQUATION EXPRESSED IN TERMS OF LIGHT, OR PURE ELECTROMAGNETIC WAVE-FORM — THE KEY TO THE UNIVERSE, THE WHOLE OF EXISTENCE, TO THE SEEN AND THE UNSEEN, TO FORMS, SOLIDS, LIQUIDS AND GASES — TO THE STARS AND

THE BLACKNESS OF SPACE ITSELF — ALL CONSISTING OF VISIBLE AND INVISIBLE WAVES OF LIGHT. ALL OF CREATION IS LIGHT.

It was now necessary to refine my calculations and attempt to discover a way to practically apply this initial equation. Although the results obtained so far were more than satisfactory, I still had a feeling that the unified theory was not quite complete. Even at this stage I had a vague idea that matter and antimatter were geometrically connected and that the equations should indicate this. Much more work was necessary and much more time went by before the harmonic geometrics were discovered which proved the correlation. There had to be an extension of the equation which so far I had missed that would produce the necessary harmonics for movement in space-time.

When I look back on my work during that period, it amazes me that I was able to discover the fundamental equations which have been the basis of my research up until the present time, considering the very roughness of the values I was working with and the limited range of my knowledge.

This must also have been the thought of two mysterious gentlemen who accosted me in a hotel in Gisborne, New Zealand, many years ago when I was on an overnight stopover while flying for the local airline.

The crew and I had finished our dinner and were relaxing in the lounge watching television when the elder of the two tapped me on the shoulder and asked very politely if I could spare some time for a chat. He would have been in his sixties and appeared to be a fairly respectable-looking gentleman, so I agreed and followed him out into the larger lounge where his companion was standing by the house bar. We sat down and after a few pleasantries the older man started questioning me about my research. This was not long after I had published my second book in the 1970s.

I gradually realised that this man was highly educated and was possibly a scientist because of his obvious knowledge of mathematics and physics. He asked me to explain how I had discovered the unified equations I had published in my book and what I believed would be the applications of the equations in the future.

Up to this stage during the questioning, his companion, a big man I estimated to be in his early fifties, had just looked on without saying a word. He had obviously been drinking and suddenly he became very agitated and started making very rude comments to me, some of them being: "How could a mug like you possibly have discovered this?" and

"How could you know all this? Where did you get this information?" He became so angry that he was almost dancing up and down in his rage.

The older man became very embarrassed by these antics, I think possibly because his companion had given the game away and shown their concern over the fact that I had published the information. It appeared that I had stumbled into a very secret area of research.

Shortly after this outburst, which to me was quite comical, the elder one of the two politely made some excuses and they quickly left the lounge. I checked with the office and found that they were not stopping at the hotel, and I realised then that the encounter had not happened by chance. They had turned up at the hotel, knowing I was there that night, specifically to confront and question me. I knew then that I had struck a nerve somewhere and that people high up in scientific circles were interested in my activities and research. Since that time I have been approached many times by strangers who profess to have a casual interest in my work, but when they ask the usual specific questions they tend to indicate their obvious connection with the intelligence groups. This has never worried me as I always carry out my work in the open and give information freely to anyone interested.

In the polar areas of the grid, the geometric values of some of the coordinates appeared to be doubled up. The coordinate of 2545.584412 was doubled in the diagonals of the polar squares, and all of its associated harmonics and other factors appeared to be doubled when the pattern was projected onto a flat plane.

I reasoned that the way to check this idea was to increase the values of 'c' in the equation and observe the changing harmonic of 'E' to see what relative values might emerge. I thought at the time that a direct antigravitational harmonic might become evident, but my recent research has proved this line of thought to be incorrect. In terms of mathematical values, I found what I was hunting for in the form of two more equations. In the case of one of the equations, I erroneously believed that the derived harmonic value related to the reciprocal of gravity. I know now that what I had hold of was an equation related to the magnetic field of the Earth.

The Earth is simply a huge magnet, a dynamo, wound with magnetic lines of force as its coils, tenescopically counted to be 1257 to the square centimetre in one direction, and 1850 to the square centimetre in the other direction (eddy currents).

The spectroscope shows that there is an enormous magnetic field around the Sun, and it is the present conclusion of the best minds that magnetic lines of force from the Sun envelop the Earth and extend to the Moon, and that EVERYTHING, NO MATTER WHAT ITS FORM ON THIS PLANET, EXISTS BY REASON OF MAGNETIC LINES OF FORCE.

This I agree with, according to my own research. We are taught in our schools and universities that the magnetic field passes through one magnetic pole, then through the Earth and out the other magnetic pole. I disagree with this explanation. I believe that the magnetic lines of force enter the Earth at the poles, then carry out a looped path through the Earth before passing out the opposite poles.

The flow is not in one pole and out the other, but in both poles and out both poles, although the field intensity both ways is unbalanced.

If we can visualise one line of force so that we can trace out its path, we can form an analogy by imagining it to be similar to a piece of string. First of all, we make a loop in the piece of string. Now imagine it being fed through a fixed position with the loop remaining stationary relative to a fixed point. With the length of string as the axis, we can now make the loop revolve in a path which is at 90° to the movement of the string. The loop in fact would trace out a spherical-shaped form in space.

The lines of force of the magnetic field would form a lattice, or grid pattern, due to the spin of the planetary body. A good analogy would be an ordinary machine-wound ball of string. The length of string has taken on the form of a ball and at the same time has formed a criss-cross pattern. If we again visualise this as a physical body being formed in space, then we can now imagine a small vortex being created at all the trillions of points where the lines of force cross each other in the lattice pattern. Each vortex would manifest as an atomic structure and create within itself what we term a gravitational field.

The gravitational field, in other words, is nothing more than the effects of relative motion in space. Matter is drawn towards a gravitational field just as a piece of wood, floating on water, is drawn towards a whirlpool. The gravitational fields created by the vortical action of every atom would combine to form the field of the completed planetary body. The world grid that I speak of is the natural grid that is formed by the lattice pattern of the interlocking lines of magnetic force.

The unbalanced fields of 1257 lines of force per square centimetre in one direction and 1850 in the other do not tell us very much in themselves.

But if we use the information to calculate the field strength over an area which has a harmonic relationship with the unified fields of space, and if the basic information is correct, we should find some mathematical values of great importance.

In my previous publications I demonstrated that there was correlation with the unified fields, within a small margin of error, due to the known conversion factors at the time. I was also not aware then that within a certain fixed range the light and gravity factors were variable, and that relativity factors would be evident in the latest and more accurate calculations. Fractional errors are still found in the conversions in relation to the given quantities, but these are so small that I am sure that the theoretical harmonic associations will stand the test when more accurate computing and conversion factors are available.

It appears now that the magnetic field strengths and areas change in conjunction with the light and gravity factors according to the change in latitude on the Earth's surface. During these changes the harmonic relationships remain constant.

The basic unit for harmonic calculation is the geodetic inch, or one seventy-two thousandths of a minute of arc—one minute of arc being 6,000 geodetic feet (6,076 British feet). If we take the values 1257 and 1850 lines of magnetic force per square centimetre and make a fractional correction to allow for the curvature of the Earth's surface (the given square centimetre area would have fractionally curved sides), we can then establish a theoretical field density of 1257.139035 lines of force in one direction and 1850.900532 lines of force in the other. This will allow the calculation of the field densities for one square geodetic inch in the north and south pole areas, which can be related mathematically to light and gravity factors shown in the matter and antimatter tables later in this book.

Field A: 1850.900532 lines of force per square centimetre
Converts to: 12245.69798 lines of force per square geodetic inch

Field B: 1257.139035 lines of force per square centimetre
Converts to: 8317.32698 lines of force per square geodetic inch

The fields would be in opposition to each other.

The combined field density is equal to:
                  20574.234 lines of force per square geodetic inch

The difference in field density is equal to:

3928.371 lines of force per square geodetic inch

or, Field A - Field B.

We can now formulate another equation in order to demonstrate the association of the Earth's magnetic field with the speed of light.

Harmonic Equation 2:

$$\text{Field (A - B)} = [2c + \sqrt{(1/2c)}](2c)^2$$
$$= 3928.371 \text{ harmonic}$$
$$\text{Where 'c'} = 144000 - 90.9345139$$
$$= \mathbf{143909.0655}$$

The reduction of light speed of 90.9345139 minutes of arc per grid second creates a very interesting factor.

The whole system of universal harmonics is based on the geometrics of the circle, the circumference of which can be divided by its radius into six equal parts. Therefore, six is the fundamental harmonic of all circular and spherical forms, and basic values can be shifted up or down the harmonic scale by multiplying or dividing by this number. Base 10 is also a part of the harmonic process and decimal points can be moved back and forth without altering the series of numbers. Zeros before and after a number series can be ignored in harmonic calculation. It takes a while to get used to these concepts but after a few practice calculations the process becomes evident.

I have had many arguments with the academics over this, but the proof of this secret mathematical system is being made evident every day by the activities of their own associates. Constructions are appearing which comply with the harmonic values. Ancient constructions also comply with the harmonic values. These secrets have been handed down through the ages.

So, if we multiply the value of 90.9345139 by the six harmonic, seven times:

$$90.9345139 \times 6 \times 6 \times 6 \times 6 \times 6 \times 6 \times 6 = 25455844$$

The result is a harmonic of 2545.5844 which is the distance in minutes of arc of each *Eltanin*-type aerial from the grid poles, and also the reciprocal harmonic of 3928.371, the difference in field density of fields "A" and "B".

It has been found that the value 143,909.0655 minutes of arc per grid second for the speed-of-light factor has a direct geometric association with electromagnetic transmission and reception. It was years after I published this particular equation that I found this out by accident while checking other data.

In my earlier publications I demonstrated how a third harmonic equation could be formulated by use of what I thought at the time to be a constant speed-of-light factor at the Earth's surface. I have now discovered that the speed of light is not a constant, and that different values within a set range can be entered into the equation which will give particular harmonic results. The value I used was 143,795.77 minutes of arc per grid second. This, in fact, was very close to 143,791.36 minutes of arc per grid second which can now be regarded as the reciprocal harmonic of gravity acceleration at the Earth's equator.

It is only in recent times that I finally cracked this secret. When I published my second book, *Harmonic 695: The UFO and Antigravity*, I could not understand the reason for the antagonism I caused amongst the establishment. It was then that I began to get particular attention from the intelligence groups and the academics. One particular visitor from Britain was insistent that I knew far more than I was admitting to. He got very angry when I tried to convince him that my knowledge was still limited to the published data. There was something in my book that they obviously were aware of and I wasn't.

It was only many years later when, because of a sudden hunch, I decided to check the gravity acceleration values in the textbooks and convert them into geometric equivalents in grid time. I found the following table for the variation of gravity with latitude at sea level, in one of my research books:

Table 1 - Variations of 'g' with latitude at sea level

Latitude	'g' metres/sec^2	Latitude	'g' metres/sec^2
0°	9.78039	50°	9.81071
10°	9.78195	60°	9.81918
20°	9.78641	70°	9.82608
30°	9.79329	80°	9.83059
40°	9.80171	90°	9.83217

The values were in metres per second squared, and I decided to convert these progressively into British feet, geodetic feet, minutes of arc or nautical miles, and degrees, based on grid time. I started off with the value at the equator of 9.78039 metres per second squared, and when I found the value for degrees, or 60 nautical miles per grid second squared, I got a very pleasant surprise:

0.000069545205 degrees per grid second squared.

The previous speed-of-light harmonic reciprocal of 695 published in my books was within about 5/100,000,000ths of the true value of gravity acceleration in geometric terms. No wonder the secret groups were getting uneasy about my findings. It was becoming obvious now that gravity and the so-called speed of light were harmonic reciprocals of each other. As gravity increased, the speed of light decreased, and vice versa. Light was therefore not a 'speed' in the true sense. It is an acceleration or deceleration according to geometric position. Because of relativity, it always appears to us as a constant factor. A little bit of thought will show that as the gravity and light values vary, then all the physical processes will vary in direct ratio, including our measuring instruments. All the readings will appear to remain constant. Time itself would also alter in relation to the gravity and light factors.

It did not take me long to calculate a rough conversion table for the full 90 degrees from the equator to the poles. This was then extended harmonically to include the speed-of-light factors up to the maximum of 144,000 minutes of arc per grid second.

I passed these initial tables to the government authorities in New Zealand for the files, and continued to work on them in order to increase the accuracy.

It was around this time that I was visited by a young man from America, Mr Rodney Maupin. Rodney is an expert computer programmer and had been following my work for a number of years. He decided to visit me in New Zealand during October 1990 and spent almost a week with me and my family. I showed him much of the research I had been doing and did my best to teach him the basics of the harmonic mathematical system used in my work. He already had a fairly good knowledge of the world energy network from the study of my books and had no trouble understanding the information I passed on to him. From that time on we have maintained contact and worked together to computerise all the mathematical data discovered in my research.

Programs were created to calculate great-circle tracks and distances over the Earth's surfaces, and the tables I had produced that unified gravity and light harmonics were very accurately calculated to fifteen decimal places. (See harmonic unified table 2.)

The values we read on our instruments are those calculated at zero latitude, or the equator, because of relativity. When the light factors are converted back into normal measurements (kilometres per second, etc.), we see that the values match those in the textbooks. Table 2 would show the harmonics of gravity and visible light. Harmonic Unified Table 3 is produced by a fractional shift in the gravity harmonic and can be associated with electromagnetic propagation.

When I originally calculated Table 2, I had great difficulty trying to fit the harmonic value of 143,909.0655 minutes of arc per grid second into the series. Each time I tried, the table would show slight errors, and no matter how I juggled the values back and forth on the computer I could not get it to fit. The secret eventually lay in what is now called the "Lamb shift".

The uncertainty principle, stated by Werner Heisenberg in 1927, indicated that it is impossible to know the position and momentum of an electron at the same time because of the inherent fluctuations in the fabric of nature itself. We are only able to work in terms of probability waves which only give an indication of the size and shape of an electron's orbit as it fluctuates within an atom. This fuzziness means that the energy of an atomic structure could change or fluctuate to another value. In other words, there is no such thing as absolute rest in the whole Universe. According to quantum theory, any type of oscillator would not completely come to rest. It would continue to jiggle randomly about its resting point with what is termed zero-point energy.

It has been demonstrated that one effect of zero-point fluctuations in an electromagnetic field is to jiggle the electrons slightly in their atomic orbits, which leads to a shift in frequency of transitions of approximately 1,000 megahertz. This is known as the "Lamb shift", named after the American physicist Willis Lamb.

It is said that the zero-point fluctuations could have some connection with gravity. Soviet physicist Andrei Sakharov suggested that gravity may be a secondary effect associated with other non-gravitational fields, brought about by changes in the zero-point energy of the vacuum due to the presence of matter.

It appears from this that the harmonic of gravity is not an absolute. It can vary fractionally with the zero-point fluctuation. This was possibly the answer I was seeking. Could the unified harmonic table be split into two due to the fractional fluctuation of the gravity value? A couple of years went by before I discovered what I believe to be the answer.

By trial and error I found that if I subtracted the speed-of-light value for the gravitational reciprocal, 143791.3643831903, from the 143909.0654859587 harmonic, the difference of 117.7011027684 was close to three times the harmonic of 39.2837100659, or 117.8511301977.

Working on the theory of a Lamb shift at the gravitational value, I decided to subtract the true harmonic of 117.8511301977 from 143909.0654859587 and set up a new value for the speed of light gravitational reciprocal:

This proved to be 143,791.214356539 minutes of arc per grid second.

The new harmonic for gravitational acceleration, or reciprocal of 143,791.214356539, was:

0.00006954527816 degrees per grid second squared.

The difference between the two gravitational factors would now be:

0.00006954527816
- 0.00006954520560
0.00000000007256

The square root of harmonic 72560:
269.3696345

More accurate computing could possibly bring this value to the harmonic of:

26944444444˙

Which brings us to **Harmonic Unified Equation 3:**

$$E = \sqrt{[(2c + \sqrt{1/2c})(2c)^2]}$$

If the maximum value of 'c', or 144,000 minutes of arc per grid second is reduced by the harmonic of phi (1618.034) and entered into this equation, the result for 'E' is the 26944444˙ harmonic.

$$
\begin{array}{ll}
144000.0000 & \\
-\quad 161.8034 & \\
\hline
143838.1966 & = \text{the harmonic of 'c'}
\end{array}
$$

Therefore,

287676.3932	= the harmonic of '2c'

Therefore,

$$E = \sqrt{[287676.3932 + \sqrt{(1/287676.3932)}(287676.3932)^2]}$$

Using harmonics,

$$E = \sqrt{[(2876763932 + 5895869843)\,(827577072)]}$$
$$= \sqrt{(8772633775 \times 827577072)}$$
$$= \sqrt{7260030574}$$
$$E = 26944444˙ \text{ harmonic}$$

Other values for 'E' can be derived from Harmonic Unified Equation 3 when the speed-of-light factor is altered harmonically between the ranges of gravity, 143791.214355761, and 144,000, the maximum.

Speed-of-Light Harmonic		Energy Harmonic
143791.214355761	gravity	2693567886
143791.3643831903	gravity	26935706
143860.9095887935	in air	2694867949
143891.3649196305	in vacuum	26954363
143909.0655	electromagnetic	26957666
144000	maximum	2697463486

We now have two unified tables which allow for visible light propagation and electromagnetic propagation, theoretically separated by a Lamb shift related to Harmonic Equation 3.

In Equations 2 and 3, the values for 'c' have been doubled to allow for antimatter which pervades our whole Universe. The scientists tell us that antimatter does exist but say that matter and antimatter are two separate forms of reality. They also say that if matter and antimatter come in contact with each other, they will cause an explosion. If both forms exist somewhere in space, we are not told where the boundary is. Space is not empty, and I believe that our Universe could not exist under these conditions. We are now told that there is more matter in the Universe than can be accounted for, and the latest term for this is "dark matter" or matter that cannot be seen.

As I have stated in my previous publications, natural law is not erratic. The Universe does not rely on chance to manifest within itself the physical substances which we perceive and call reality. A very strict, ordered system of mathematical progressions is necessary to create the smallest speck of matter from the primeval matrix of space.

During my years of research into the complexities of the Earth grid system, I have gradually built up a picture in my mind of the possible geometric combinations necessary to form matter from resonating, interlocking wave-forms.

Matter and antimatter are formed by the same wave-motions in space. The waves travel through space in a spiralling motion, and alternately pass through positive and negative stages. Matter is formed through the positive stage, or pulse, and antimatter through the negative pulse. Each spiral of 360° forms a single pulse. The circular motion of an electron about the nucleus of an atom is therefore an illusion. The relative motion of the nucleus and electrons through space gives the illusion of circular motion. The period during the formation of anti-matter is completely undetectable, since obviously all physical matter is manifesting at the same pulse rate, including any instruments or detectors used to probe atomic structures. The period or frequency rate between each pulse of physical matter creates the measurement that we call time, as well as the speed of light, at the particular position in space of which we are aware at any given moment.

If the frequency rate of positive and negative pulses is either increased or decreased, then time and the speed of light vary in direct proportion. This concept would explain time as a geometric, as Einstein theorised it to be.

A rough analogy of physical existence can be made by reference to a strip of motion picture film. Each frame or static picture on the film strip may be likened to a single pulse of physical existence. The division between one frame and the next represents a pulse of antimatter. When viewed as a complete strip, each frame would be seen as a static picture (say, one at either end of the strip), then the past and the future can be viewed simultaneously. However, when the film is fed through a projector, we obtain the illusion of motion and the passage of time. The divisions between the static pictures are not detected by our senses because of the frequency or speed of each projection on the movie screen. But by speeding up or slowing down the projector, we can alter the apparent time-rate of the actions shown by the film.

To continue this analogy, our consciousness is the projector. The conscious 'I am' part of our individuality passes from one pulse of physical matter to the next within the framework of the physical structure which we term our body, thus giving the illusion of constant reality and the passing of time.

It is logical to assume that we have a twin stream of consciousness on the antimatter side of the cycle, which in fact creates a mirror image of our own individual personality. (This postulate has already been put forward by scientists.) The frequency of manifestation of both streams of consciousness, that is, the plus and minus 'I am', would position our awareness of the illusion of reality at a particular point in space and time. In other words, if the frequency of pulse manifestation is altered even fractionally, our awareness of reality in the physical sense will shift from one spatial point to another. In fact, we would travel from one point in space to another without being aware that we have traversed distance in the physical sense. This would be the ultimate method for space travel.

The theory outlined above explains why light has been described as being caused by both a wave motion and a pulse. Both explanations are correct. A pulse of light is manifested when the energy level of an atomic structure is altered by outside influences (the theory of Max Planck). In the physical plane, the electron of the atomic structure appears to jump from its orbit. According to my belief, the electron does not jump orbit. This is the illusion we obtain, since we are not equipped to perceive the path of the electron during the antimatter cycle. What actually happens is that the radius of the spiralling motion is increased or decreased in order to absorb or release the energy imparted to or removed from the atomic structure. If the energy is imparted, then the electron must extend orbit in order to maintain balance in the system, and vice versa. Light, or any other radiant energy above or below light frequency, is therefore manifested by undetectable changes in the radius of the spiral motion of the electron during the antimatter cycle.

If this hypothesis is correct, movement from one point in space to another point, regardless of apparent distance—in other words, true space travel—is completely feasible. By manipulating the frequency rate of the matter-antimatter cycle, the time and speed of light can be varied in direct proportion to any desired value.

All the mathematical evidence amassed so far indicates that the maximum number of individual elements to be found in the Universe will be 144. Each of these elements will have, in theory, six isotopes, which will make up a completed table of separate substances numbering 1008.

An isotope is an atom of the same element which has a different nuclear mass and atomic weight. Mathematically, the progression would create 144 octaves of separate substances, giving a theoretical value of 1152. The difference between the total number of substances (1008), and the harmonic value in octaves, would be 144—the light harmonic.

Once the precipitation of physical matter has occurred, the build-up of substances takes place according to a very well-ordered mathematical sequence. Light-waves, guided seemingly by superior intelligence, form intricate interlocking grid patterns which graduate from the simple to the more complex, as the elements from hydrogen at the lower end of the scale to element 144 come into being.

When we think of reality we must think of mass in relation to any physical manifestation, and the smallest particle of physical matter that we are aware of is the electron. Therefore electron mass must be the starting point in our quest for a feasible theory to explain the structure of matter.

The average radius of action of the electron around the atomic nucleus must also have a constant harmonic value in order to set up a system of expanding spheres which encompass the structure of each element. As the number of protons in the nucleus increases with the build-up of each element, the spherical space which houses the electron shell must expand to accommodate an equal number of electrons.

Although the protons and electrons are nothing more than extremely concentrated wave-forms, we consider them as physical particles in order to build up a picture of our model.

As each electron cloud or shell expands outward from the nucleus, we find that it can accommodate only eight electrons. The shell is then filled up and another expansion must take place in order to form a new shell or harmonic zone, which again builds up to a maximum of eight electrons. As the magnitude of the harmonic resonance intensifies, the heavier elements are progressively produced until we reach a maximum of 144. The light harmonic is then equal and the cycle has been completed. The whole series is a repetition of octaves of wave-forms forming more and more complex structures.

In my earlier work I had assumed that the harmonic radius of the atom was equal to the mass ratio of the proton and electron. I now realise that although I was on the right track, the theoretical model demonstrated was partly in error. This necessitated another search into the physics books, and I now feel that the following calculations based on the experimental values are getting close to the truth.

It would be logical to base the harmonic interaction on the geometric structure of the hydrogen atom. If harmonic equivalents can be derived from the basic values established by experimental physics and remain within the laid-down tolerances, then almost certainly a new theory should be evident—especially if the harmonic values closely match those found in the unified equations previously demonstrated.

The distance given between the electron and the proton in the hydrogen atom is approximately 5.3×10^{-11} metre. (See *Physics—Part 2*, Halliday & Resnick.)

I have discovered, according to recent information, that a close theoretical value of $5.29724146 \times 10^{-11}$ metres could be associated with the unified tables:

$$5.29724146 \times 10^{-11} \text{ metres}$$

$$= 208.5528148 \times 10^{-11} \text{ British inches}$$
$$= 205.9441884 \times 10^{-11} \text{ geodetic inches}$$

The radius of the hydrogen atom would therefore be tuned to the harmonic value of 20594.41884. This would be harmonically equivalent to the number of magnetic lines of force per square geodetic inch in this geometric arrangement.

The diameter of the hydrogen atom would be:

	$= 205.9441884 \times 10^{-11}$
Multiplied by 2	$= 411.8883768 \times 10^{-11}$
Squared	$= 169652.0349$ harmonic
Squared	$= 2.87818812^{10}$ harmonic
Divided by 2	$= 1.439090655^{10}$ harmonic

The diameter of the hydrogen atom would then be harmonically related to the electromagnetic propagation value of 143,909.0655 minutes of arc per grid second. (See electromagnetic unified tables.)

If we now calculate the circumference of the hydrogen atom in terms of harmonic geodetic feet, then:

Diameter	$= 411.8883768 \times 10^{-11}$ geodetic inches
	$= 34.32403140 \times 10^{-11}$ geodetic feet

Therefore, circumference

$$= 107.8321249 \times 10^{-11} \text{ geodetic feet}$$

Now if we allow spacing on this circumference for eight electron positions, we have harmonically:

$107.8321249 \div 8 \qquad = 13.47901561$ units

But an electron has only half-a-spin value, the other half taking place during the antimatter cycle, so harmonically:

$13.47901561 \times 2 \qquad = 26.95803122$

Allowing for slight inaccuracies in the conversion values, it is almost certain that the geometric harmonics of the hydrogen atom would comply with the geometric energy value derived from Unified Equation 3 when the value for 'c' is equal to 143,909.0655 minutes of arc per grid second, namely, the 26957666 harmonic.

More work on the computer should show a perfect match.

We can now use the hydrogen atom as a baseline to form a theory regarding the formation of the complete atomic table of elements. I believe that the harmonic radius of 205.9441884 units would remain constant throughout the whole range of elements, the orbits of electrons in all substances taking up harmonically spaced positions to the power of ten. In other words, by shifting the decimal point to the right or left of this basic harmonic, the orbital radius of all electrons can be calculated. (See Diagram 4.)

This would apply to the whole range of 144 elements and their isotopes. Physical reality, as we perceive it, is manifested by the concentrated interlocking of harmonic wave-forms, which are built up progressively from a foundation of fundamental wave-packets.

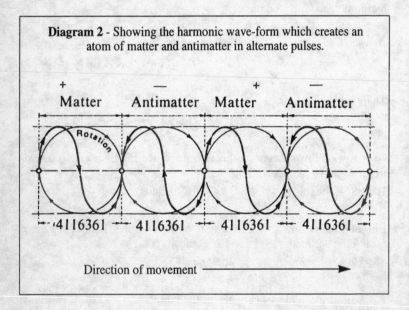

Diagram 2 - Showing the harmonic wave-form which creates an atom of matter and antimatter in alternate pulses.

+ — + —
Matter Antimatter Matter Antimatter

Rotation

4116361 — 4116361 — 4116361 — 4116361

Direction of movement ⟶

Diagrams 2, 3 and 4 show how matter and antimatter are created out of the same wave-forms. As the electron is moving through a spiral in each matter and antimatter pulse, it travels through a space of more than 360 degrees during each cycle. The theoretical number of degrees would be 370.95199; the double cycle, 741.90399.

Diagram 3

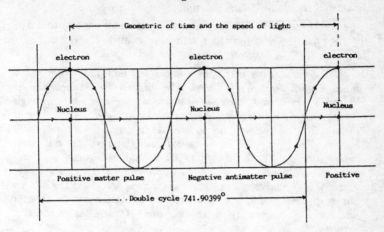

Diagram 4

Showing the harmonic wave formation of a basic element and the six associated isotopes

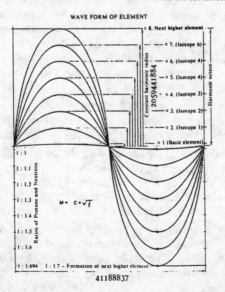

The reciprocal harmonic of 370.95199 is 2.6957666^{-3}. As we see, this would be the value of 'E' in relation to Unified Equation 3 if the value of 'c' equals 143,909.0655 minutes of arc per grid second.

A quote I found in a book I was reading recently appears to confirm my theory of the double matter-antimatter cycle. The book is called *Beyond the Occult*, by Colin Wilson.

> *"Human beings are accustomed to the fact that if they turn round through 360° (through a full circle) they find themselves facing in the direction they started from. Not so an electron. By passing it through a certain type of magnetic field, its 'axis of spin' can be tipped through 360°, which ought to restore it to its original position. But it doesn't. The electron has to be turned through yet another full circle before it behaves as it did before. We cannot distinguish the difference between the two circles. The electron can—which seems to suggest that in the subatomic world a full circle is not 360° but 720°. In our world we have lost half the degrees we ought to have. Or to put it another way, there may be another dimension in the subatomic world."*

As my own research has shown me that physical reality is manifested by the harmonic nature of light, it appears logical that a vehicle constructed to the principles of harmonics will be required to set up the space-time fields necessary. If this is so, then the first criterion will be that the vehicle must resonate in perfect harmony with the complete table of elements in our physical Universe. If it does not, then it would be more than probable that any element or particle of matter not in harmonic resonance within the vehicle structure or payload would be left behind when the space-time field was activated. The results would be embarrassing, to say the least.

It would be impractical to construct a vehicle made from an alloy of the whole range of 144 elements in the theoretical atomic table. Apart from this, such an alloy is no doubt a physical impossibility.

The clue which suggests a method of overcoming this problem is the way that matter is built up in octaves of wave-forms. If an octave of elements could be combined which would set up a resonating field tuned to all the elements in the table and the unified fields of space, then maybe we would have a method of crashing the time barrier.

I put forward the following proposal for consideration. If an octave of elements is the answer, let us make a selection from the theoretical table of 144. If we divide 144 by 8, we get divisions of 18 units. Therefore we will select each of the elements we require, 18 units apart, as follows:

Atomic Number	Element
18	argon
36	krypton
54	xenon
72	hafnium
90	thorium
108	X — undiscovered element
126	Y — undiscovered element
144	Z — undiscovered element

It can be seen that the total harmonic value of the atomic numbers of the combined elements is 648. The square root of this number is 25.455844, the harmonic of which is found in the polar sections of the world grid system. The harmonic 25455844 is also directly associated with the Earth's magnetic field. Three recently discovered elements have atomic numbers of 116, 124 and 126. What we now need are numbers 108 and 144.

We would then be ready for the harmonic conquest of space.

The following theoretical tables, calculated by computer, demonstrate the unified nature of all the natural forces and are based on the assumption that the Earth is a perfect sphere.

The indications are that gravity, the speed of light and the Earth's magnetic field are all manifested from the same natural forces. Gravity, in fact, is the reciprocal harmonic of the speed of light, and vice versa.

If the theory can be proved, the knowledge could open up unlimited progress in many scientific fields—unlimited amounts of energy being one area of research.

The conversion factors used to convert the values into geometric units are as follows:

1 metre	= 39.37007874 British inches
12 inches	= 1 British foot
6,076 British feet	= 1 minute of arc
6,000 geodetic feet	= 1 minute of arc
1 kilometre	= 3,280.839 British feet

One minute of grid time equals 8/9ths of one minute of normal time.

Because of relativity, the equatorial values will always be indicated on all instruments of measurement. As the gravity and light speeds change, the geometric dimensions change in direct mathematical ratio. This relativistic change makes the speed of light appear to be a constant. It is, in fact, an acceleration or deceleration according to position in space-time.

The difference between the speed of light (gravitational reciprocal) at the equator, and the speed of light (gravitational reciprocal) at the pole, appears to be a very important harmonic factor. (See column G.) The computed value of 757.7876168 minutes of arc per grid second difference would allow the following harmonic calculations:

757.7876168 x6x6x6x6x6	= 5892556.507
Reciprocal	= 1.6970562^{-7}
Squared	= 2.88^{-14}

2.88^{-14} is the harmonic of twice the speed of light maximum (288,000 minutes of arc per grid second).

757.7876168 x 2	= 1515.575233 (matter-antimatter)
1515.575233 x6x6x6x6x6x6x6	= 25455184408
Reciprocal	= 3.928371^{-10}

The harmonic 3928371 is related to the Earth's magnetic field.

Conversion Values for Unified Gravity and Light Tables:

X: Degrees Latitude (equator to pole): 0° to 90°

A: Gravity acceleration (metres/sec²): 9.78039102718 at the equator

B: Gravity acceleration (feet/sec²): 32.0878970708 at the equator
A x 39.37007874 ÷ 12

C: Gravity acceleration (geodetic feet/sec²): 31.6865343030 at the equator
B x 6000 ÷ 6076

D: Gravity acceleration (geodetic feet/grid sec²): 25.0362740172 at the equator
C x 8 x 8 ÷ (9 x 9)

E: Gravity acceleration (mins.arc/grid sec²): 4.172712336^{-3} at the equator
D ÷ 6000

F: Gravity acceleration (degrees/grid sec²): 6.954520560^{-5} at the equator
E ÷ 6000 (creates the harmonic reciprocal of the speed of light—gravity)

G: Gravitational speed of light (min/grid sec): 143791.3643831903 at the
10/**F** harmonic equator

H: Harmonic linkage between speed of light (gravity) and speed of light (air) at the Earth's surface: 69.54520560 at the equator
10000000/**G**

I: Speed of light, in air, at the Earth's surface (mins/grid sec): 143860.9095887935 at equator
G + H Converts to 299728.59 km/sec (299729 standard)

J: Harmonic linkage between speed of light, in air, and speed of light, in vacuum: 30.4547943968 at the equator
K - I

K: Speed of light, in vacuum, at the Earth's surface (mins/grid sec): 143891.3649196305 at equator
G + 100.0005364402
Converts to 299792.0425 km/sec (299792.5 standard)

L: Harmonic linkage between speed of light, in vacuum, and theoretical speed of light, maximum (mins/grid sec): 108.635616809 at the equator

M: Speed of light (theoretical maximum) at the Earth's surface (mins/grid sec): 144000 at the equator
G + (**H** x 3) Converts to 300018.3793 km/sec
(Perfect conversion would be 144000 and 300000)

Table 2 demonstrates the conversion of gravity acceleration into 'speed'-of-light harmonics that are directly related to those published in the classical physics books. Due to relativity, we always read the values for the 'speed' of light calculated on our instruments at the equator, giving the illusion of a constant speed instead of an acceleration or deceleration.

The speed of light in air (column I) is calculated to be:

143,860.9096 minutes of arc per grid second.

Converted into classical values, this becomes:

143,860.9096 x 6,076 x 9 ÷ (3,280.839 x 8)   = 299,728.59 km/sec
Textbook value   = 299,729.00 km/sec

The 'speed' of light in vacuum (column K) is calculated to be:

143,891.3649 minutes of arc per grid second.

Converted into classical values, this becomes:

(143,891.3649 x 6,076 x 9) ÷ (3,280.839 x 8) = 299,792.0425 km/sec
Textbook value   = 299,792.5 km/sec

This demonstrates that the gravitational conversion values are very accurate.

Table 2

Gravitational values (standard textbook) conversion to geometric harmonics of light. Due to relativity, the values at 0 degrees (the equator) are always read on all instruments.

Visible Light Spectrum

X	A	B	C	D	E	F
0	9.780391027184701	32.08785707081595	31.68653430297822	25.03627401716798	0.004172712336194664	0.00006954520560324439
1	9.780406809705001	32.08794885073819	31.68658543522534	25.03631441795582	0.004172719069659304	0.00006954531782765506
2	9.780454138037330	32.088104127419007	31.68673876966991	25.03643557109721	0.004172739261849536	0.00006954565436415893
3	9.780532954519408	32.088363271167785	31.68699411949755	25.03663732098572	0.004172772888164287	0.00006954621480273811
4	9.780643163125490	32.088724288846946	31.68735117360381	25.03691944581042	0.004172819907635069	0.00006954699846058449
5	9.780784629583367	32.089188417268	31.68780949637327	25.03728157855642	0.004172880262975904	0.00006954800438293174
6	9.780957181537950	32.08975453260482	31.68836853120950	25.03772328391862	0.004172953086053103	0.00006954923134421839
7	9.781160608761263	32.090421944475480	31.68902759521541	25.03824402584921	0.004173040670974868	0.00006955067784958114
8	9.781394663408571	32.091189840579730	31.68978588602301	25.03884316920337	0.004173140528200561	0.00006955234213567602
9	9.781659060320337	32.09205728451554	31.69064247977176	25.03951999401720	0.004173253306695933	0.00006955422217782554
10	9.781954373696653	32.09302321971671	31.69159633283415	25.04027364569612	0.004173378940943353	0.00006955563156824892
11	9.782279558854696	32.09408664933595	31.69264628308712	25.04110323601945	0.004173517206003242	0.00006955862010005403
12	9.782630900935752	32.09524573797819	31.69379105132803	25.04200774425919	0.004173667957376531	0.00006956176943037857
13	9.783013082116268	32.09649961324235	31.69502924283313	25.04298606841136	0.004173831011401894	0.00006956385019003156
14	9.783423633367347	32.09784656747817	31.69635934905678	25.04403701653870	0.004174006169423116	0.00006956676949033857
15	9.783862055695041	32.09928495962940	31.69777974946945	25.04515930822278	0.004174192180377930	0.00006956988696728549
16	9.784327812749766	32.10081303773426	31.69928871353202	25.04635157612407	0.004174393925461011	0.00006957331098212638
17	9.784820340477077	32.10242893857309	31.70088440280424	25.04761236764779	0.004174602061274632	0.00006957670021243987
18	9.785339035809249	32.10413069491150	31.70256487318450	25.04894014617368	0.004174823375785613	0.00006958038929642689
19	9.785883267795246	32.10591623292404	31.70432807727851	25.05033329562746	0.004175055549271244	0.00006958425915452074
20	9.786452373372898	32.10778377220767	31.70617186689368	25.05179011705180	0.004175298352841967	0.00006958830865909944
21	9.787045659174499	32.10972985293471	31.70809399565639	25.05330883607419	0.004175551472679031	0.00006959325245445052
22	9.787662402372685	32.11175328862430	31.71009212174081	25.05488760236943	0.004175814600349016	0.00006959691006156339
23	9.788301851560878	32.11385121903175	31.71216381076210	25.05652449254401	0.004176087415409001	0.00006960145692348334
24	9.788963227668734	32.11602108815202	31.71430653866230	25.05821751202947	0.004176369585338245	0.00006960615975563741
25	9.789645724911349	32.11826025233383	31.71651769486553	25.05996459841227	0.004176660766402046	0.00006961012773367643
26	9.790348511770958	32.12056598350052	31.71879458541855	25.06176362304675	0.004176960603841126	0.00006961601006401877
27	9.791070732010034	32.12293547247387	31.72135439678099	25.06361239409855	0.004177268732349758	0.00006962114553316263
28	9.791811505714461	32.12536583239653	31.72353439670493	25.06550865910493	0.004177584776520814	0.00006962641294201356
29	9.792569930365589	32.12785410229931	31.72599154270834	25.06745010781893	0.004177908351303155	0.00006963180585505258
30	9.793345081939808	32.13039725045869	31.72850288063729	25.06943437482342	0.004178239062470754	0.00006963731770784590
31	9.794136016034328	32.13299217859059	31.73106535081335	25.07145904261795	0.004178576507102992	0.00006964294158504987
32	9.794947696017786	32.13563572512397	31.73367583126133	25.07352164445533	0.004178920274075565	0.00006964867123459275
33	9.795761359204292	32.13832466893041	31.73633114151292	25.07561966736823	0.004179269945461372	0.00006965449907602287
34	9.796593788049449	32.14105573507037	31.73902804648161	25.07775055524473	0.004179625092540788	0.00006966041820901312
35	9.797438041366936	32.14382559503588	31.74176326040409	25.07991171192422	0.004179985285320703	0.00006966642142201173
36	9.798293009564133	32.14663087455424	31.74453345084356	25.08210050437022	0.004180350084061703	0.00006967250140102838
37	9.799157893895304	32.14946815582449	31.74733552474966	25.08431426587627	0.004180719041312712	0.00006967864507385650
38	9.800031397730802	32.15233399205644	31.75016522257055	25.08655029931500	0.004181091716552500	0.00006968461942354167
39	9.800912253784075	32.15522486168228	31.75301994241173	25.08880588042408	0.004181467664573347	0.00006969121744562245
40	9.801800240691673	32.15813727261047	31.75589592423681	25.09107826112538	0.004181846376854230	0.00006969743961423716
41	9.802693424754368	32.16106766651696	31.75878966410496	25.09336467287305	0.004182227445478842	0.00006970379075798071
42	9.803591001821644	32.16401247316812	31.76169763643988	25.09566233002657	0.004182610388337762	0.00006971017313896270
43	9.804491878334108	32.16696810477070	31.76461629832524	25.09796843324644	0.004182994738015948	0.00006971669008026581
44	9.805394956712457	32.16993096634284	31.76754209382111	25.10028017389569	0.004183380028815948	0.00006972340982244750
45	9.806299136654918	32.17289743010144	31.77047145829635	25.10259473248107	0.004183765788746845	0.00006972942981247740
46	9.807203316677338	32.17586389986003	31.77340082277159	25.10490929206644	0.004184151548677740	0.00006973585914462900
47	9.808106395055727	32.17882675543218	31.77632661826745	25.10722103171749	0.004184536836195983	0.00006974228064359201
48	9.809007271568190	32.18178238703474	31.77924528015281	25.10952713493555	0.004184921189159525	0.00006974868648593208
49	9.809904848635442	32.18472719368592	31.78215325248774	25.11182479208908	0.004185304132014846	0.00006975505886659410
50	9.810798032698163	32.18765758759240	31.78504699235589	25.11411120383575	0.004185685200639459	0.00006976142001065764
51	9.811685735549078	32.19056989852060	31.78792297418098	25.11638358453806	0.004186063930570943	0.00006977673217927238
52	9.812566875659034	32.19346087814644	31.79077769402216	25.11863916564714	0.004186439860941189	0.00006977399768235315
53	9.813440379494530	32.19632670437838	31.79360767384303	25.12087519908586	0.004186812533180976	0.00006978020888634960
54	9.814305182825702	32.19916389564863	31.79640946574914	25.12308896059191	0.004187181493431986	0.00006978635822386644
55	9.815160232032899	32.20196926516699	31.79917965618861	25.12527753503791	0.004187546292172985	0.00006979243820288308
56	9.816004485340386	32.20473912513250	31.80191487011109	25.12743890717141	0.004187906484952901	0.00006979844114588168
57	9.816836314185544	32.20747019089745	31.80461177507978	25.12956979759390	0.004188261632932316	0.00006980436054887194
58	9.817655043720483	32.21015913507890	31.80726708533136	25.13166782050873	0.004188611303418122	0.00006981018393030204
59	9.818462257355506	32.21280268161255	31.80987756577935	25.13373042234418	0.004188955057030696	0.00006981591738960364
60	9.819253191450025	32.21539760974418	31.81244003595541	25.13575509013761	0.004189292515022935	0.00006982154191704891
61	9.820028340324244	32.21794075795356	31.81495137388436	25.13773935714319	0.004189623226190532	0.00006982705376984221
62	9.820786767675374	32.22042902780635	31.81740851988777	25.13968080503725	0.004189946800972875	0.00006983244668288124
63	9.821527541379801	32.22285938772901	31.81980848031172	25.14157707086359	0.004190262845143932	0.00006983771408573220
64	9.822249761618876	32.22522887670235	31.82214833117414	25.14342584191537	0.004190570073652562	0.00006984284956087602
65	9.822952548478487	32.22753460786905	31.82442522172718	25.14522486654987	0.004190870811091645	0.00006984784685152740
66	9.823635045721101	32.22977377205086	31.82663637793040	25.14697195293266	0.004191161992155444	0.00006985269986325740
67	9.824296421828958	32.23194364117112	31.82877910583060	25.14866497250813	0.004191447161087037	0.00006985740721003613
68	9.824935871017148	32.23404157157857	31.83085079484388	25.15025018662270	0.004191769170987083	0.00006986194961831305
69	9.825552614215336	32.23606500726637	31.83284892093631	25.15188062888794	0.004191980104814657	0.00006986633508024430
70	9.826145900016936	32.23801148299520	31.83477104969901	25.15339934791033	0.004192233224651732	0.00006987055374419536
71	9.826715005594588	32.23987862727883	31.83661483931419	25.15485619593461	0.004192476022822445	0.00006987460047037408
72	9.827259237580810	32.24166416529138	31.83837804340821	25.15624931824846	0.004192708237970076	0.00006987847032846734
73	9.827777932912758	32.24336592162978	31.84005851378846	25.15757709731430	0.004192929516219056	0.00006988215860365093
74	9.828270456460068	32.24498182296610	31.84165420306067	25.15883788883806	0.004193139648139676	0.00006988566080232739
75	9.828736216947953	32.24650990057347	31.84316316571224	25.16003015673935	0.004193338359456559	0.00006988897265760931
76	9.829174639620848	32.24794829272470	31.84458356753591	25.16115244842344	0.004193525408070573	0.00006989209015094426
77	9.829585191273567	32.24929524696052	31.84591367375957	25.16220339655077	0.004193700560191195	0.00006989500934480624
78	9.829967372454083	32.25054912222648	31.84715186526446	25.16318172070294	0.004193863620117157	0.00006989772700339236
79	9.830320717535139	32.25170839086332	31.84829663350508	25.16403788958305	0.004194014371490447	0.00006990023952548407
80	9.830644796020181	32.25277164048616	31.84934658738551	25.16491581926601	0.004194152636544336	0.00006990254394270566
81	9.830932130694317	32.25373755568732	31.85030043682093	25.16569480094913	0.004194278669604000	0.00006990463744770632
82	9.831203609981264	32.25460501962357	31.85115703056968	25.16634629575876	0.004194391042939127	0.00006990651748281877
83	9.831437664628570	32.25537291544806	31.85191532137738	25.16694543911292	0.004194490906518820	0.00006990818207654438
84	9.831641091851884	32.25604032759804	31.85253745803819	25.16746618104351	0.004194557676480585	0.00006990962880676949
85	9.831813643806048	32.25660644293460	31.85313341963943	25.16790788710671	0.004194651314517785	0.00006991086110534946
86	9.831955110284244	32.25707037173241	31.83539172429889	25.16827001915173	0.004194711069858619	0.00006991186163141303
87	9.832065318870427	32.25743214852503	31.85394879709515	25.16855213597642	0.004194758689329402	0.00006991264482215673
88	9.832144135352504	32.25769072378381	31.85420414692279	25.16875389386452	0.004194792215644152	0.00006991320526073588
89	9.832191463684834	32.25784600946408	31.85435748136736	25.16875467000631	0.004194812507834385	0.00006991354179923939
	9.832207246205135	32.25789778938692	31.85440861361447	25.16891544779415	0.004194819241299026	0.00006991365402165504

Table 2 (continued)

G	H	I	J	K	L	M
143791.3643831903	69.5452056032438	143860.9095887935	30.4553308369650	143891.3649196305	108.6350803695386	144000.0000000000
143790.1323488617	69.5453178276507	143860.6776666894	30.4552186125365	143891.1328853019	108.6354170427658	143999.7683023447
143790.6365330640	69.5456543641589	143859.9821874282	30.4548220760392	143890.4370695042	108.6342665228691	143999.0734961565
143789.2777969893	69.5462148027381	143858.8240117921	30.4543216374586	143889.2783334295	108.6381079679956	143997.9164413975
143787.6575747185	69.5469984605849	143857.2045731791	30.4535379796289	143887.6581111587	108.6404589415470	143996.2985701003
143785.5778713640	69.5480043829174	143855.1258757470	30.4525320577204	143885.5784078042	108.6434767085884	143994.2218845128
143783.0412604739	69.5492313442184	143852.5904918181	30.4513050959794	143883.0417969743	108.6471575924661	143991.6889545066
143780.0508807007	69.5506778495811	143849.6015585503	30.4498585906126	143880.0514171409	108.6514971085417	143988.7029142495
143776.6104317405	69.5523421366760	143846.1627738772	30.4481943035207	143876.6109681807	108.6564899698133	143985.2674581505
143772.7241695484	69.5542221782555	143842.2783917263	30.4463142623174	143872.7247059886	108.6621300912602	143981.3868360819
143768.3969008367	69.5563156824892	143837.9532165191	30.4442075722309	143868.3974372769	108.6684106072644	143977.0658478841
143763.6339768654	69.5586201000543	143833.1925969655	30.4419163401471	143863.6345133056	108.6753239559631	143972.3098371656
143758.4412865334	69.5611326229422	143828.0024191564	30.4394038172613	143858.4418229736	108.6828614286205	143967.1246844023
143752.8252487812	69.5638501900315	143822.3890989712	30.4366862501744	143852.8257852214	108.6910141299013	143961.5167993513
143746.7928043157	69.5667694903852	143816.3595738061	30.4337665498054	143846.7933407559	108.6997720303591	143955.4931127868
143740.3514066710	69.5698869672854	143809.9212936383	30.4306494729242	143840.3519431113	108.7091244616604	143949.0610675729
143733.5090126169	69.5731988225668	143803.0822114395	30.4273376176424	143833.5095490571	108.7190600275062	143942.2286090846
143726.2740719296	69.5767010212438	143795.8507729508	30.4238354189728	143826.2746083698	108.7295666235150	143935.0041749933
143718.6555165411	69.5803892964269	143788.2359058375	30.4201471437001	143818.6560529813	108.7406314493654	143927.3966844304
143710.6627490813	69.5842591545207	143780.2470082358	30.4162772856698	143810.6632855215	108.7522410233505	143919.4155265648
143702.3056308306	69.5883058006994	143771.8939367113	30.4122305595832	143802.3061672708	108.7643812019087	143911.0705484728
143693.5944691014	69.5925245446503	143763.1869936461	30.4080118955622	143793.5950055416	108.7770371937368	143902.3720427354
143684.5400040649	69.5969100658175	143754.1369140715	30.4036264336187	143784.5405405051	108.7901935795380	143893.3307340846
143675.1539500438	69.6014569224834	143744.7548519673	30.3990795167046	143775.1539314840	108.8038343302615	143883.9577658142
143665.4462062907	69.6061597556743	143735.0523606463	30.3943764843230	143765.4467427309	108.8179428262576	143874.2646855576
143655.4303922714	69.6110127733671	143725.0414050448	30.3895236668460	143755.4309287116	108.8325018798932	143864.2634305915
143645.1282657756	69.6160100640187	143714.7342925398	30.3845263761759	143745.1188189160	108.8474937514677	143853.9661266678
143634.5226557756	69.6211455391628	143704.1471113147	30.3793909010412	143734.5231022158	108.8629001772708	143843.3860023930
143623.6562743541	69.6264129420135	143693.2826872962	30.3741236981865	143723.6568107943	108.8787023858458	143832.5350131802
143612.5327672280	69.6318058550525	143682.1645730813	30.3687305851490	143712.5333036682	108.8948811249575	143821.4281847932
143601.1657133847	69.6373177078450	143670.8030310926	30.3632187323283	143701.1662498249	108.9114168613460	143810.0766650083
143589.5690745603	69.6429417850498	143659.2120163454	30.3575946551570	143689.5696110005	108.9282889149617	143798.4978599155
143577.7570876794	69.6486712459275	143647.4055891440	30.3518652056274	143677.7576241196	108.9454772635654	143786.7031013831
143565.7442469828	69.6544990760228	143635.3987460588	30.3460373618649	143665.7447834230	108.9629607878742	143774.7077442109
143553.5452858670	69.6604182090132	143623.2057740008	30.3401182311936	143653.5458223072	108.9807181868237	143762.5265404940
143541.1751584589	69.6664214220174	143610.8415798809	30.3341150189501	143641.1756948991	108.9987278258195	143750.1744227249
143528.6490209521	69.6725014010288	143598.3215223532	30.3280350391804	143628.6495573923	109.0169677628728	143737.6665251552
143515.9822127289	69.6786507385819	143585.6608634674	30.3218857016749	143615.9827491691	109.0354157754336	143725.0181649445
143503.1902372922	69.6848619425616	143572.8750992347	30.3156744976862	143603.1907373224	109.0540493874287	143712.2448231198
143490.2887430348	69.6911274456226	143559.9798704804	30.3094089945618	143590.2892794750	109.0728458946769	143699.3621253716
143477.2935038677	69.6974396142715	143546.9909434419	30.3030968299559	143577.2940403079	109.0917824025091	143686.3858227104
143464.2203997356	69.7037907579870	143533.9241904936	30.2967456822254	143564.2209361758	109.1108358337369	143673.3311720096
143451.0853970631	69.7101731389670	143520.7955701821	30.2903633012339	143551.0859334833	109.1299829766795	143660.2159164600
143437.9045290159	69.7165789812351	143507.6211079971	30.2839574589743	143537.9050654561	109.1492005035107	143647.0542659596
143424.6938760240	69.7230004802658	143494.4168765043	30.2775359599272	143524.6944124642	109.1684650006064	143633.8628774649
143411.4695458889	69.7294298124742	143481.1894690473	30.2711066277466	143511.4700823291	109.1877529971534	143620.6578353262
143398.2476542012	69.7358591446289	143467.9831534558	30.2646772552977	143498.2481906414	109.2070409936714	143607.4552316351
143385.0443046718	69.7422806436591	143454.7865853154	30.2582557965310	143485.0448411120	109.2263054907671	143594.2711486027
143371.8755695413	69.7486864859327	143441.6242560272	30.2518499542784	143471.8761059815	109.2455230175983	143581.1216289991
143358.7574700704	69.7550688669141	143428.5125389374	30.2454675728790	143458.7580065106	109.2646701605408	143568.0226766712
143345.7059571361	69.7614201065596	143415.4673771467	30.2391164295500	143445.7064937563	109.2837235917686	143554.9902171681
143332.7368919546	69.7677321792739	143402.5046241338	30.2328042609425	143432.7374283948	109.3026600976009	143542.0400884924
143319.8660269561	69.7739976823534	143389.6400246385	30.2265387578181	143419.8665633963	109.3214566068491	143529.1880200032
143307.1089868319	69.7802088863460	143376.8891957183	30.2203275586363	143407.1095232721	109.3400902188441	143516.4496134910
143294.4812497763	69.7863582386643	143364.2676080002	30.2141782163249	143394.4817862165	109.3585382314050	143503.8403244479
143281.9981289449	69.7924382028039	143351.7905671478	30.2080982371543	143381.9986653852	109.3767816845583	143491.3754435536
143269.6745741506	69.7984414158816	143339.4731955664	30.2020950243680	143369.6752905908	109.3947878074541	143479.0700783982
143257.5260538162	69.8043605488719	143327.3304143650	30.1961758912395	143357.5265902564	109.4125452064036	143466.9391354628
143245.5667372069	69.8101883903025	143315.3769255973	30.1903404988789	143345.5672734671	109.4300287307124	143454.9973023779
143233.8112769586	69.8159178398494	143303.6271967985	30.1846186003533	143333.8118133988	109.4472170793451	143443.2590304782
143222.2738919235	69.8215419170048	143292.0954338406	30.1789945235150	143322.2744283637	109.4640893109317	143431.7385176747
143210.9685303510	69.8270537698422	143280.7955841208	30.1734826703641	143310.9690667912	109.4806248693203	143420.4496916605
143199.9088534214	69.8324468288124	143269.7411001042	30.1680897573242	143309.9093898616	109.4968036084319	143409.4061934700
143189.1082191505	69.8377140857320	143258.9459332362	30.1628223544852	143299.1087559357	109.5126058169990	143398.6213614077
143178.5796666824	69.8428495608762	143248.4225162432	30.1576868793451	143278.5802031226	109.5280122424301	143388.1082153650
143168.3359009845	69.8478468515274	143238.1834778361	30.1526895866363	143268.3364374247	109.5430041143845	143377.8794415391
143158.3892779649	69.8526998692574	143228.2419778242	30.1478367094813	143258.3898144051	109.5575616575601	143367.9473775527
143148.7519002825	69.8574027014147	143218.6091927240	30.1431373077667	143248.7523264627	109.5716716644054	143358.3239981268
143139.4350520484	69.8619496183305	143209.2971016667	30.1385868218786	143239.4355884886	109.5853124147397	143349.0209009034
143130.4502878904	69.8663350802430	143200.3166229707	30.1342013599621	143230.4508243306	109.5984688005410	143340.0492931312
143121.8083172952	69.8705537441953	143191.6788710394	30.1299826960021	143221.8088537354	109.6112479239803	143331.4197852578
143113.5195433406	69.8746007037048	143183.3941810110	30.1259359698167	143213.5200797808	109.6232657921273	143323.1433447518
143105.5939403710	69.8784703284794	143175.4724106995	30.1220611174045	143205.5944768112	109.6348745452124	143315.2293513565
143098.0410424465	69.8821586036599	143167.9232010502	30.1183778365351	143198.0415788867	109.6459393707628	143307.6875182575
143090.8699323180	69.8856608023279	143160.7555931203	30.1148756378675	143190.8704687582	109.6564459667716	143300.5269147250
143084.0892309386	69.8889726576093	143153.9782035562	30.1115637825860	143184.0897573788	109.6663815326174	143293.7561449114
143077.7070875214	69.8920901345099	143147.5991776558	30.1084463057500	143177.7076239616	109.6757339631831	143287.3835792490
143071.7311701521	69.8950094348635	143141.6261795870	30.1055270053299	143171.7317065923	109.6844918643765	143281.4161984567
143066.1686569671	69.8977270019536	143136.0663839691	30.1028094382419	143166.1691934073	109.6926445656572	143276.0618379730
143061.0262279037	69.9002395248409	143130.9264674286	30.1002969153639	143161.0267643439	109.7001821343147	143270.7269463782
143056.3100570309	69.9025439424560	143126.2126009733	30.0979924577875	143156.3105934711	109.7070951870134	143266.0176889581
143052.0258054675	69.9046374470625	143121.9304429146	30.0958989931369	143152.0263419077	109.7133759010176	143261.7397178087
143048.1786148950	69.9065174882187	143118.0851323832	30.0940189519871	143148.1791513352	109.7190160244645	143257.8981673596
143044.7731616996	69.9081817753136	143114.6812834447	30.0923546648918	143144.7736381096	109.7240088857361	143254.4976461953
143041.8133513592	69.9096282806742	143111.7227981398	30.0909081595305	143141.8138807974	109.7283484018408	143251.5422385812
143039.3029149732	69.9108524196308	143109.2137021520	30.0896811982840	143139.3034514134	109.7320292856894	143249.0354806951
143037.2448031029	69.9118611643103	143107.1566642672	30.0886752258816	143137.2453395431	109.7350470527308	143246.9803865959
143035.6414842827	69.9126448221567	143105.5541291049	30.0878916180580	143135.6420207229	109.7373980262782	143245.3794187492
143034.4948812714	69.9132052607358	143104.4080865321	30.0873311947122	143134.4954177116	109.7390793419509	143244.2329887715
143033.8063690375	69.9135417923974	143103.7199108347	30.0869946437398	143133.8069054777	109.7400889515120	143243.5464994292
143033.5767731903	69.9136540216504	143103.4904272119	30.0868824185543	143133.5773096305	109.7404256247391	143243.3177352552

Table 3

----Suspected correction to allow for (the Lamb shift)
between column F (visible light spectrum) and
column F' (electromagnetic spectrum)

Electromagnetic Spectrum

X	F	-> ~	F'	G'	H'	I'
0	0.000006954520560324439	0.000000000072561	0.000006954527801642439	143791.2143565390	39.283710065919308	143830.4980666050
1	0.000006954531782765506	0.000000000072561	0.000006954539038865506	143790.9823226947	39.283710065919308	143830.2660327606
2	0.000006954654364154893	0.000000000072561	0.000006954572692515893	143790.2865083489	39.283710065919308	143829.5702184149
3	0.000006954642148027381	0.000000000072561	0.000006954628736373811	143789.1277746922	39.283710065919308	143828.4114847581
4	0.000006954699846058449	0.000000000072561	0.000006954707102158449	143787.5075558023	39.283710065919308	143826.7912658682
5	0.000006954800438253174	0.000000000072561	0.000006954807694393174	143785.4278567875	39.283710065919308	143824.7115668534
6	0.000006954923134421839	0.000000000072561	0.000006954930390521839	143782.8912511903	39.283710065919308	143822.1749612562
7	0.000006955067784958114	0.000000000072561	0.000006955050750410581	143779.9008776567	39.283710065919308	143819.1845877226
8	0.000006955234213667602	0.000000000072561	0.000006955214657676602	143776.4604358752	39.283710065919308	143815.7441459411
9	0.000006955422217782554	0.000000000072561	0.000006955422554437388	143772.5741817917	39.283710065919308	143811.8578918576
10	0.000006955631568248922	0.000000000072561	0.000006955638824348922	143768.2469221085	39.283710065919308	143807.5306321744
11	0.000006955862010005403	0.000000000072561	0.000006955869266105403	143763.4840080744	39.283710065919308	143802.7677181403
12	0.000006956113262294219	0.000000000072561	0.000006956120518394219	143758.2912385758	39.283710065919308	143797.5750386417
13	0.000006956385019003156	0.000000000072561	0.000006956392275103156	143752.6753025398	39.283710065919308	143791.9590126057
14	0.000006956676949038527	0.000000000072561	0.000006956684205138528	143746.6428706587	39.283710065919308	143785.9265807246
15	0.000006956988696728549	0.000000000072561	0.000006956995952828549	143740.2014864510	39.283710065919308	143779.4851965169
16	0.000006957319882256684	0.000000000072561	0.000006957327138358448	143733.3591066697	39.283710065919308	143772.6428167356
17	0.000006957670122438700	0.000000000072561	0.000006957735822344388	143726.1241810732	39.283710065919308	143765.4078911392
18	0.000006958038929642689	0.000000000072561	0.000006958046185742689	143718.5056415700	39.283710065919308	143757.7893516409
19	0.000006958425915452074	0.000000000072561	0.000006958433171552074	143710.5128907850	39.283710065919308	143749.7966008509
20	0.000006958830588069944	0.000000000072561	0.000006958837844169944	143702.1557899631	39.283710065919308	143741.4395000290
21	0.000006959252454465052	0.000000000072561	0.000006959329710565052	143693.4446463998	39.283710065919308	143732.7283564658
22	0.000006959610065817600	0.000000000072561	0.000006959682567581176	143684.3902002441	39.283710065919308	143723.6739101000
23	0.000006960145692348234	0.000000000072561	0.000006960105249484334	143675.0036107950	39.283710065919308	143714.2873208609
24	0.000006960615975563741	0.000000000072561	0.000006960623231663741	143665.2964422811	39.283710065919308	143704.5801523470
25	0.000006961101277336743	0.000000000072561	0.000006961108533436743	143655.2806491431	39.283710065919308	143694.5643592090
26	0.000006961601006401877	0.000000000072561	0.000006961608262501877	143644.9685608449	39.283710065919308	143684.2522709108
27	0.000006962114553916243	0.000000000072561	0.000006962121810016263	143634.3728662317	39.283710065919308	143673.6565762976
28	0.000006962641294201356	0.000000000072561	0.000006962648550301357	143623.5065974597	39.283710065919308	143662.7903075256
29	0.000006963180585505258	0.000000000072561	0.000006963187841605258	143612.3831135173	39.283710065919308	143651.6668235832
30	0.000006963731770784590	0.000000000072561	0.000006963739026884590	143601.0160833635	39.283710065919308	143640.2997934294
31	0.000006964294217850498	0.000000000072561	0.000006964301434604987	143589.4194687051	39.283710065919308	143628.7031787710
32	0.000006964867123459275	0.000000000072561	0.000006964874313955273	143577.6075064369	39.283710065919308	143616.8912165028
33	0.000006965449907602287	0.000000000072561	0.000006965457163702287	143565.5946907696	39.283710065919308	143604.8784008355
34	0.000006966041820901312	0.000000000072561	0.000006966049077001312	143553.3957550686	39.283710065919308	143592.6794651345
35	0.000006966642142201173	0.000000000072561	0.000006966649398301173	143541.0256534298	39.283710065919308	143580.3093634957
36	0.000006967250541012838	0.000000000072561	0.000006967253962028838	143528.4995420151	39.283710065919308	143567.7832520810
37	0.000006967865073854520	0.000000000072561	0.000006967872329954520	143515.8327601745	39.283710065919308	143555.1164702404
38	0.000006968486194254167	0.000000000072561	0.000006968493450354167	143503.0408113788	39.283710065919308	143542.3245214447
39	0.000006969112744562245	0.000000000072561	0.000006969120000662245	143490.1393439881	39.283710065919308	143529.4230540540
40	0.000006969743961423716	0.000000000072561	0.000006969751217523717	143477.1441318805	39.283710065919308	143516.4278419464
41	0.000006970379075798071	0.000000000072561	0.000006970386331898071	143464.0710549676	39.283710065919308	143503.3547650335
42	0.000006971017313896230	0.000000000072561	0.000006971024569956270	143450.9360796206	39.283710065919308	143490.2197898666
43	0.000006971657898123512	0.000000000072561	0.000006971665154223512	143437.7552390319	39.283710065919308	143477.0389490979
44	0.000006972300048026581	0.000000000072561	0.000006972307304126581	143424.5446135380	39.283710065919308	143463.8283236040
45	0.000006972942981244728	0.000000000072561	0.000006972950237344744	143411.3203109268	39.283710065919308	143450.6040209927
46	0.000006973585914462900	0.000000000072561	0.000006973591705627900	143398.0984467554	39.283710065919308	143437.3821568213
47	0.000006974228064365972	0.000000000072561	0.000006974235320465972	143384.8951247012	39.283710065919308	143424.1788347671
48	0.000006974868648593208	0.000000000072561	0.000006974877264169713	143371.7264169713	39.283710065919308	143411.0101270372
49	0.000006975506886691410	0.000000000072561	0.000006975514142791410	143358.6083447933	39.283710065919308	143397.8920548592
50	0.000006976142001065764	0.000000000072561	0.000006976149257657764	143345.5568590107	39.283710065919308	143384.8405690766
51	0.000006976773217927238	0.000000000072561	0.000006976780474027238	143332.5878208669	39.283710065919308	143371.8715308728
52	0.000006977399768235315	0.000000000072561	0.000006977407024135315	143319.7169825796	39.283710065919308	143359.0006926455
53	0.000006978020888634960	0.000000000072561	0.000006978028144734960	143306.9599689874	39.283710065919308	143346.2436790533
54	0.000006978635822386644	0.000000000072561	0.000006978643078486644	143294.3322581924	39.283710065919308	143333.6159682584
55	0.000006979244382028830	0.000000000072561	0.000006979251076388308	143281.8491633188	39.283710065919308	143321.1328733847
56	0.000006979844143588168	0.000000000072561	0.000006979851376880168	143269.5258414477	39.283710065919308	143308.8095242136
57	0.000006980436054887194	0.000000000072561	0.000006980443310987194	143257.3771390713	39.283710065919308	143296.6608491372
58	0.000006981018839030204	0.000000000072561	0.000006981026095130204	143245.4178473242	39.283710065919308	143284.7015573901
59	0.000006981591783984493	0.000000000072561	0.000006981599040084493	143233.6624115122	39.283710065919308	143272.9461215781
60	0.000006982154170489100	0.000000000072561	0.000006982161447088491	143222.1250504582	39.283710065919308	143261.4085650761
61	0.000006982705376984221	0.000000000072561	0.000006982712633084221	143210.8197123825	39.283710065919308	143250.1034224484
62	0.000006983244668280124	0.000000000072561	0.000006983251924388124	143199.7600584373	39.283710065919308	143239.0437685032
63	0.000006983771408573220	0.000000000072561	0.000006983778664673220	143188.9594464508	39.283710065919308	143228.2431566768
64	0.000006984284956087602	0.000000000072561	0.000006984292212698602	143178.4309160201	39.283710065919308	143217.7146260860
65	0.000006984784685152740	0.000000000072561	0.000006984791941252740	143168.1871716663	39.283710065919308	143207.4708816723
66	0.000006985269986925740	0.000000000072561	0.000006985277243025741	143158.2405692519	39.283710065919308	143197.5242793178
67	0.000006985740270141146	0.000000000072561	0.000006985747526241146	143148.6031013312	39.283710065919308	143187.8868113971
68	0.000006986194961831305	0.000000000072561	0.000006986202179313305	143138.2863827110	39.283710065919308	143178.5700927769
69	0.000006986635080024130	0.000000000072561	0.000006986646074612440	143128.3016372162	39.283710065919308	143169.5853472821
70	0.000006987055374419536	0.000000000072561	0.000006987062630553536	143118.6596845709	39.283710065919308	143160.9433946368
71	0.000006987460047037408	0.000000000072561	0.000006987467303137408	143109.3709278317	39.283710065919308	143152.6546378976
72	0.000006987847032846794	0.000000000072561	0.000006987854288946794	143100.4453413223	39.283710065919308	143144.7290513882
73	0.000006988215860365093	0.000000000072561	0.000006988223116465093	143091.8924590830	39.283710065919308	143137.1761691489
74	0.000006988566080232794	0.000000000072561	0.000006988566020783794	143083.7213638441	39.283710065919308	143130.0050739120
75	0.000006988897265760931	0.000000000072561	0.000006988904521865231	143076.0476454599	39.283710065919308	143123.2243866128
76	0.000006989209013450954	0.000000000072561	0.000006989212718509954	143067.5585463877	39.283710065919308	143116.8422564476
77	0.000006989500943486324	0.000000000072561	0.000006989508199586325	143071.5826142004	39.283710065919308	143110.8663514863
78	0.000006989772720001562	0.000000000072561	0.000006989779965472606	143066.0201397845	39.283710065919308	143105.3498088504
79	0.000006990023992340790	0.000000000072561	0.000006990031084087900	143060.8777213976	39.283710065919308	143100.1614314635
80	0.000006990254394240560	0.000000000072561	0.000006990261650340560	143056.1615603160	39.283710065919308	143095.4452703819
81	0.000006990464374706925	0.000000000072561	0.000006990471005202625	143051.8773176468	39.283710065919308	143091.1610277127
82	0.000006990651748821878	0.000000000072561	0.000006990659004921879	143048.0301350610	39.283710065919308	143087.3138451269
83	0.000006990818173751366	0.000000000072561	0.000006990825429851366	143044.6244289049	39.283710065919308	143083.9089708
84	0.000006990963820867641	0.000000000072561	0.000006990841676641	143041.6648849187	39.283710065919308	143080.9489308708
85	0.000006991085524196308	0.000000000072561	0.000006991092780296308	143039.1544535640	39.283710065919308	143078.4381636299
86	0.000006991186116431033	0.000000000072561	0.000006991193372531033	143037.0963459660	39.283710065919308	143076.3800560319
87	0.000006991264448221567	0.000000000072561	0.000006991271738315671	143035.4930304739	39.283710065919308	143074.7767405398
88	0.000006991320526207588	0.000000000072561	0.000006991327782317588	143034.3464298426	39.283710065919308	143073.6301399085
89	0.000006991341793712974	0.000000000072561	0.000006991361443563974	143033.6579190379	39.283710065919308	143072.9416293038
90	0.000006991365402165043	0.000000000072561	0.000006991372658265043	143033.4283236673	39.283710065919308	143072.7120337332

Table 3 (continued)

J'	K'	L'	M'	N'	O'
39.28371006591931	143865.7817766709	39.28371006591931	143909.0654867360	90.93451404147989	144000.0000007782
39.28371006591931	143869.5497428265	39.28371006591931	143908.8334528924	90.93451404147989	143999.7679669339
39.28371006591931	143868.8539284808	39.28371006591931	143908.1376385467	90.93451404147989	143999.0721525881
39.28371006591931	143867.6951948240	39.28371006591931	143906.9789048899	90.93451404147989	143997.9134189314
39.28371006591931	143866.0749759341	39.28371006591931	143905.3586860001	90.93451404147989	143996.2932000415
39.28371006591931	143863.9952769193	39.28371006591931	143903.2789869852	90.93451404147989	143994.2135010267
39.28371006591931	143861.4860713221	39.28371006591931	143900.7423813880	90.93451404147989	143991.6768954295
39.28371006591931	143858.4682977886	39.28371006591931	143897.7520078545	90.93451404147989	143988.6865218959
39.28371006591931	143855.0278560070	39.28371006591931	143894.3115660729	90.93451404147989	143985.2460801144
39.28371006591931	143851.1416019235	39.28371006591931	143890.4253119894	90.93451404147989	143981.3598260309
39.28371006591931	143846.8143422403	39.28371006591931	143886.0980523062	90.93451404147989	143977.0325663477
39.28371006591931	143842.0514282062	39.28371006591931	143881.3351382721	90.93451404147989	143972.2696523136
39.28371006591931	143836.8587487076	39.28371006591931	143876.1424587735	90.93451404147989	143967.0769728150
39.28371006591931	143831.2427226716	39.28371006591931	143870.5264327375	90.93451404147989	143961.4609467790
39.28371006591931	143825.2102907905	39.28371006591931	143864.4940008564	90.93451404147989	143955.4285148979
39.28371006591931	143818.7689065828	39.28371006591931	143858.0526166488	90.93451404147989	143948.9871306902
39.28371006591931	143811.9265268015	39.28371006591931	143851.2102368674	90.93451404147989	143942.1447509089
39.28371006591931	143804.6916012051	39.28371006591931	143843.9753112710	90.93451404147989	143934.9098253124
39.28371006591931	143797.0730617068	39.28371006591931	143836.3567177727	90.93451404147989	143927.2912858142
39.28371006591931	143789.0803109168	39.28371006591931	143828.3640209827	90.93451404147989	143919.2985350242
39.28371006591931	143780.7232100949	39.28371006591931	143820.0069201608	90.93451404147989	143910.9414342023
39.28371006591931	143772.0120665317	39.28371006591931	143811.2957765976	90.93451404147989	143902.2302906390
39.28371006591931	143762.9576203759	39.28371006591931	143802.2413304418	90.93451404147989	143893.1758444833
39.28371006591931	143753.5710309268	39.28371006591931	143792.8547409927	90.93451404147989	143883.7892550342
39.28371006591931	143743.8638624129	39.28371006591931	143783.1475724788	90.93451404147989	143874.0820865203
39.28371006591931	143733.8480622749	39.28371006591931	143773.1317793408	90.93451404147989	143864.0662933823
39.28371006591931	143723.5359809767	39.28371006591931	143762.8196910426	90.93451404147989	143853.7542050841
39.28371006591931	143712.9402863635	39.28371006591931	143752.2239964294	90.93451404147989	143843.1585104709
39.28371006591931	143702.0740175915	39.28371006591931	143741.3577276574	90.93451404147989	143832.2922416989
39.28371006591931	143690.9505336491	39.28371006591931	143730.2342437150	90.93451404147989	143821.1687577565
39.28371006591931	143679.5835034953	39.28371006591931	143718.8672135612	90.93451404147989	143809.8017276027
39.28371006591931	143667.9868888369	39.28371006591931	143707.2705989028	90.93451404147989	143798.2051129443
39.28371006591931	143656.1749265688	39.28371006591931	143695.4586366347	90.93451404147989	143786.3931506761
39.28371006591931	143644.1621109014	39.28371006591931	143683.4458209673	90.93451404147989	143774.3803350088
39.28371006591931	143631.9631752004	39.28371006591931	143671.2468852664	90.93451404147989	143762.1813993078
39.28371006591931	143619.5930735616	39.28371006591931	143658.8767836275	90.93451404147989	143749.8112976690
39.28371006591931	143607.0669621469	39.28371006591931	143646.3506722128	90.93451404147989	143737.2851862542
39.28371006591931	143594.4001803063	39.28371006591931	143633.6838903722	90.93451404147989	143724.6184044137
39.28371006591931	143581.6082315106	39.28371006591931	143620.8919415766	90.93451404147989	143711.8264556180
39.28371006591931	143568.7067641199	39.28371006591931	143607.9904741858	90.93451404147989	143698.9249882273
39.28371006591931	143555.7115520123	39.28371006591931	143594.9952620782	90.93451404147989	143685.9297761197
39.28371006591931	143542.6384750994	39.28371006591931	143581.9221851653	90.93451404147989	143672.8566992068
39.28371006591931	143529.5034997525	39.28371006591931	143568.7872098184	90.93451404147989	143659.7217238598
39.28371006591931	143516.3226591638	39.28371006591931	143555.6063692297	90.93451404147989	143646.5408832711
39.28371006591931	143503.1120336698	39.28371006591931	143542.3957437538	90.93451404147989	143633.3302577772
39.28371006591931	143489.8877310586	39.28371006591931	143529.1714411245	90.93451404147989	143620.1059551660
39.28371006591931	143476.6658668873	39.28371006591931	143515.9495769532	90.93451404147989	143606.8840909946
39.28371006591931	143463.4625448330	39.28371006591931	143502.7462548989	90.93451404147989	143593.6807689404
39.28371006591931	143450.2938371031	39.28371006591931	143489.5775471691	90.93451404147989	143580.5120612105
39.28371006591931	143437.1757649251	39.28371006591931	143476.4594749910	90.93451404147989	143567.3939890325
39.28371006591931	143424.1242791425	39.28371006591931	143463.4079892084	90.93451404147989	143554.3425032498
39.28371006591931	143411.1552409387	39.28371006591931	143450.4389510046	90.93451404147989	143541.3734650461
39.28371006591931	143398.2844027114	39.28371006591931	143437.5681127773	90.93451404147989	143528.5026266188
39.28371006591931	143385.5273891192	39.28371006591931	143424.8110991851	90.93451404147989	143515.7456132266
39.28371006591931	143372.8996783243	39.28371006591931	143412.1833883902	90.93451404147989	143503.1179024316
39.28371006591931	143360.4165834506	39.28371006591931	143399.7002935165	90.93451404147989	143490.6348075580
39.28371006591931	143348.0932342795	39.28371006591931	143387.3769443454	90.93451404147989	143478.3114583869
39.28371006591931	143335.9945592031	39.28371006591931	143375.2882692690	90.93451404147989	143466.2227833105
39.28371006591931	143323.9852674560	39.28371006591931	143363.2689775219	90.93451404147989	143454.2034915634
39.28371006591931	143312.2298316440	39.28371006591931	143351.5134017099	90.93451404147989	143442.4479157514
39.28371006591931	143300.6924705900	39.28371006591931	143339.9761806559	90.93451404147989	143430.9106946973
39.28371006591931	143289.3871325143	39.28371006591931	143328.6708425802	90.93451404147989	143419.6053566217
39.28371006591931	143278.3274785691	39.28371006591931	143317.6111886350	90.93451404147989	143408.5457026765
39.28371006591931	143267.5268667427	39.28371006591931	143306.8105768086	90.93451404147989	143397.7450908501
39.28371006591931	143256.9983361519	39.28371006591931	143296.2820462178	90.93451404147989	143387.2165602593
39.28371006591931	143246.7545917382	39.28371006591931	143286.0383018041	90.93451404147989	143376.9728158455
39.28371006591931	143236.8079893838	39.28371006591931	143276.0916994497	90.93451404147989	143367.0262134911
39.28371006591931	143227.1705214630	39.28371006591931	143266.4542315289	90.93451404147989	143357.3887455704
39.28371006591931	143217.8538028428	39.28371006591931	143257.1375129080	90.93451404147989	143348.0720269502
39.28371006591931	143208.8690573480	39.28371006591931	143248.1527674139	90.93451404147989	143339.0872814553
39.28371006591931	143200.2271047027	39.28371006591931	143239.5108147686	90.93451404147989	143330.4453288101
39.28371006591931	143191.9383479636	39.28371006591931	143231.2220580295	90.93451404147989	143322.1565720709
39.28371006591931	143184.0127614541	39.28371006591931	143223.2964715200	90.93451404147989	143314.2309855615
39.28371006591931	143176.4598792148	39.28371006591931	143215.7435892807	90.93451404147989	143306.6781033222
39.28371006591931	143169.2887839779	39.28371006591931	143208.5724940438	90.93451404147989	143299.5070080851
39.28371006591931	143162.5080966787	39.28371006591931	143201.7918067446	90.93451404147989	143292.7263207861
39.28371006591931	143156.1259665135	39.28371006591931	143195.4096765794	90.93451404147989	143286.3441906209
39.28371006591931	143150.1506615522	39.28371006591931	143189.4343716181	90.93451404147989	143280.3682856596
39.28371006591931	143144.5875599163	39.28371006591931	143183.8712699822	90.93451404147989	143274.8057840237
39.28371006591931	143139.4451415294	39.28371006591931	143178.7288515953	90.93451404147989	143269.6633656368
39.28371006591931	143134.7289804478	39.28371006591931	143174.0126905137	90.93451404147989	143264.9472045552
39.28371006591931	143130.4444377786	39.28371006591931	143169.7281478445	90.93451404147989	143260.6626618860
39.28371006591931	143126.5975551928	39.28371006591931	143165.8812652587	90.93451404147989	143256.8157793001
39.28371006591931	143123.1920490367	39.28371006591931	143162.4757591026	90.93451404147989	143253.4102731441
39.28371006591931	143120.2323050506	39.28371006591931	143159.5160151165	90.93451404147989	143250.4505291579
39.28371006591931	143117.7218736958	39.28371006591931	143157.0055837618	90.93451404147989	143247.9409780832
39.28371006591931	143115.6637660978	39.28371006591931	143154.9474761637	90.93451404147989	143245.8819902051
39.28371006591931	143114.0604506057	39.28371006591931	143153.3441606716	90.93451404147989	143244.2786747130
39.28371006591931	143112.9138499744	39.28371006591931	143152.1975600403	90.93451404147989	143243.1320740818
39.28371006591931	143112.2253391697	39.28371006591931	143151.5090492356	90.93451404147989	143242.4356327713
39.28371006591931	143111.9957437991	39.28371006591931	143151.2794538650	90.93451404147989	143242.2139679065

Table 4

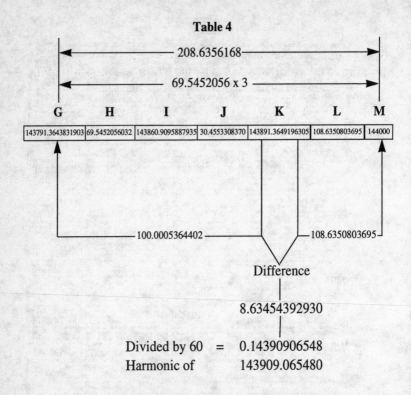

Difference

8.63454392930

Divided by 60   =   0.14390906548

Harmonic of   143909.065480

(See unified electromagnetic table)

This section of the unified table demonstrates that the difference between the speed of light (gravity reciprocal harmonic) 143791.36438319, and the speed of light (maximum) 144000, is equal to three times the harmonic of gravity acceleration, 69.5452056.

These values, calculated at the equator, are always read on our scientific instruments due to relativity. Although the term 'speed of light' is used, light, or electromagnetic propagation, is in fact an acceleration depending on position in space.

The relative value for the speed of light in vacuum, 143891.36491963, also sets up a harmonic affinity with the electromagnetic propagation value, 143909.06548, because of its relationship with the minimum and maximum values.

Table 5

Section of gravitational conversion unified table showing the relationship of the visible spectrum and the electromagnetic spectrum. Values calculated at the equator (0° latitude).

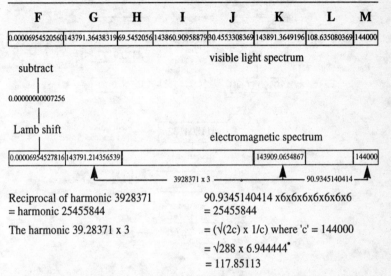

F	G	H	I	J	K	L	M
0.00006954520560	143791.36438319	69.5452056	143860.90958879	30.4553308369	143891.3649196	108.635080369	144000

visible light spectrum

subtract
|
0.00000000007256
|
Lamb shift

electromagnetic spectrum

| 0.00006954527816 | 143791.214356539 | | | | 143909.0654867 | | 144000 |

— 3928371 x 3 — 90.9345140414 —

Reciprocal of harmonic 3928371
= harmonic 25455844

The harmonic 39.28371 x 3

90.9345140414 x6x6x6x6x6x6x6
= 25455844

= ($\sqrt{(2c)}$ x 1/c) where 'c' = 144000

= $\sqrt{288}$ x 6.944444˙

= 117.85113

Earth magnetic field A - Earth magnetic field B = 3928371 harmonic. See Unified Equation 2 where 'c' is equal to 143909.065486.

When the geometric values for the speed of light in air (143860.909588 minutes of arc per grid second) and the speed of light in vacuum (143891.3649196 minutes of arc per grid second) are converted into kilometres per normal second, we get the classical values in the textbooks (299729 and 299792.5).

The tables show, without doubt, that gravity acceleration is the harmonic reciprocal of the light factors, and vice-versa. This is the information required for the harmonic penetration of deep space.

The following tables will demonstrate how the unified values of gravity, light and the Earth's magnetic field are harmonically related to matter and antimatter. For demonstration I have picked out the gravity values at the equator, fifty degrees latitude, and the north and south poles, plus the gravity value related to the speed of light—143909.0655 minutes of arc per grid second.

Table 6 - Gravity acceleration values at the equator

Table demonstrating the harmonic relationship between the Earth's magnetic field, the speed of light, and gravity acceleration.

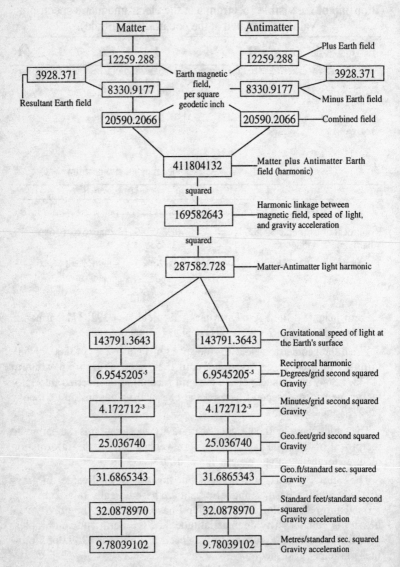

Table 7 - Gravity acceleration values at 50° latitude

Table demonstrating the harmonic relationship between the Earth's magnetic field, the speed of light, and gravity acceleration.

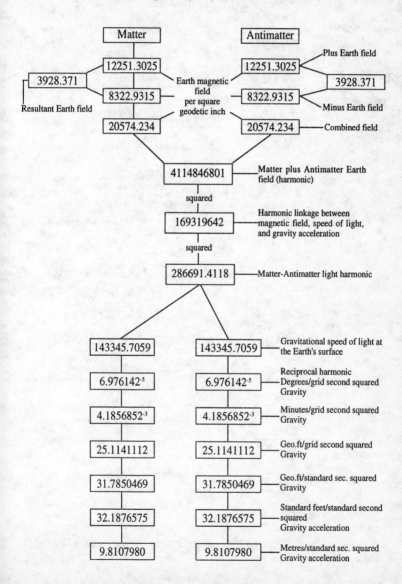

Table 8 - Gravity acceleration values at the north and south poles
Table demonstrating the harmonic relationship between the Earth's magnetic field, the speed of light and gravity acceleration.

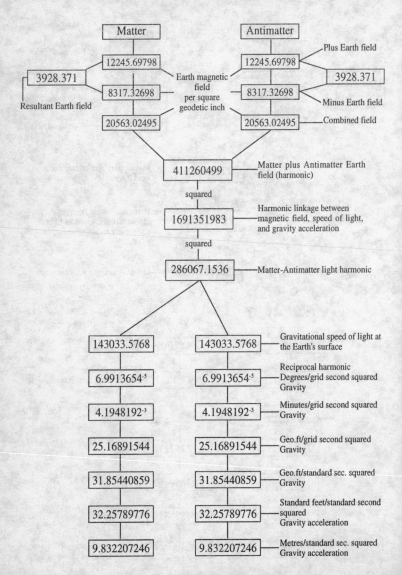

Table 9 - Matter and antimatter table for the speed-of-light value
143909.0655 minutes of arc per grid second

Table demonstrating the harmonic relationship between the Earth's magnetic field, the speed of light and gravity acceleration.

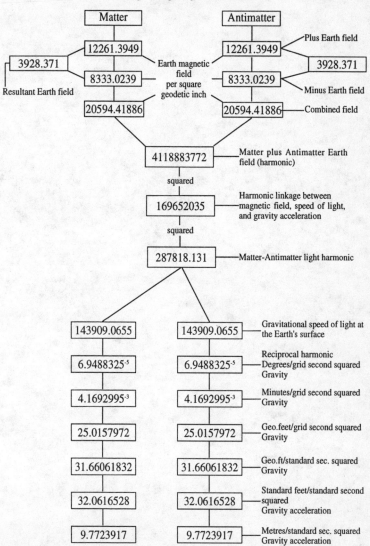

Matter	Antimatter	
12261.3949	12261.3949	Plus Earth field
3928.371	3928.371	
8333.0239	8333.0239	Earth magnetic field per square geodetic inch / Minus Earth field
Resultant Earth field		
20594.41886	20594.41886	Combined field
4118883772		Matter plus Antimatter Earth field (harmonic)
squared		
169652035		Harmonic linkage between magnetic field, speed of light, and gravity acceleration
squared		
287818.131		Matter-Antimatter light harmonic
143909.0655	143909.0655	Gravitational speed of light at the Earth's surface
6.9488325⁻⁵	6.9488325⁻⁵	Reciprocal harmonic Degrees/grid second squared Gravity
4.1692995⁻³	4.1692995⁻³	Minutes/grid second squared Gravity
25.0157972	25.0157972	Geo.feet/grid second squared Gravity
31.66061832	31.66061832	Geo.ft/standard sec. squared Gravity
32.0616528	32.0616528	Standard feet/standard second squared Gravity acceleration
9.7723917	9.7723917	Metres/standard sec. squared Gravity acceleration

Chapter Two

THE CONVERSION OF GEOMETRIC HARMONICS INTO VALUES COMPATIBLE WITH THOSE IN CLASSICAL PHYSICS

Over the years I have had a running battle with the scientific fraternity regarding my use of geometric harmonics to demonstrate the unified nature of the Universe. It has been their contention that all my conclusions must be in error because there was no way that the values I use could be equated with those in the physics books. Chance, they said, if any of my calculations appeared to be valid when compared with classical values.

I present the following mathematical evidence to demonstrate that there is a way to bridge the gap between classical values and geometric harmonics.

In physics, the standard unit for wavelength is called the angstrom unit (abbr. Å).

One angstrom unit	$= 10^{-10}$ metre
One metre	$= 39.370079$ inches
	$= 3.2808399$ feet
	$= 5.39967^{-4}$ minutes of arc
	(relative to the Earth's surface)
	(nautical mile)
$5.39967 \div 6 \div 6 \div 6 \div 6$	$= 6.944^{-8}$

It appears that the angstrom unit is equal to the reciprocal of the maximum speed of light harmonic (144000) in the geometric tables—.6944˙ (repeating).

The Coulomb Converted to Geometric Harmonics

Usually an electrician measures the flow of electricity in amperes. The number of amperes tells us how many electrons flow past a given point per second. Experiments show that if 6.25×10^{18} electrons flow past per second, we have 1 ampere. This number of electrons, 6.25×10^{18}, is called the coulomb.

To convert this value to grid time we must use the ratio of 8:9, so:

$6.25 \times 10^{18} \times 8/9$ $= 5.55555555˙ \times 10^{18}$

The harmonic value can be taken as: $5.55555555˙$

We can now associate this harmonic with geometric values:

$\sqrt{(1/5.55555555 \div 36)}$ $= 6.48$

$\sqrt{6.48}$ $= 2.455844$ harmonic (25455844)

(See grid polar sections and Earth magnetic values.)

Also, if we assume that the $5.55555555˙$ harmonic is associated with one full shell in the atomic structure, then:

$5.55555555˙ \div 8$ $= 0.69444444˙$ harmonic for each electron (light reciprocal)

The Relationship Between Electron Mass and the Harmonic Geometric Tables

Electron mass given as $= 9.11 \times 10^{-31}$ kilograms

If we assume a full shell of 8 electrons:

Total mass $= 9.11^{-31} \times 8$

                        $= 72.88^{-31}$ kilograms

This would be for one matter-cycle, and to allow for the antimatter cycle we must double the mass for a complete matter-antimatter cycle. Therefore,

72.88 x 2	= 145.76^{-31} kilograms
Reciprocal of 145.76	= 6.8605927^{-3}
6.8605927^{-3} x the 6 harmonic	= 0.041163556 harmonic
This harmonic squared	= 1.6944383 harmonic

(See matter-antimatter harmonic table.)

(π x ϕ)/3, or

(3.1415927 x 1618.034) ÷ 3   = 1694.401242 harmonic

This would give an electron mass value of 9.1100998 x 10^{-31} kilograms. This could have some significance.

The Magnetic Monopole and the Fine-Structure Constant

A few years ago a group of scientists suspended a cosmic ray detector 130,000 feet above Sioux City in Iowa, in order to intercept atomic particles coming in from deep space. Amongst a shower of heavy particles there was one that was completely different from its neighbours. After much debate the scientists considered that the strange particle must be a magnetic monopole, the basic unit of magnetism. According to theory, in order to have complete symmetry between electricity and magnetism there must be a magnetic monopole. This would be similar to the negative electron or positive proton.

All known magnetic materials seem to be dipolar in nature, and no single north or south poles have been discovered before the event of this visitor from space.

A British physicist, Paul Dirac, calculated that there should be a basic magnetic particle that carries a north or south charge 68.5 times that of the electron, or some multiple of that value—possibly 137. This single number would be associated with the speed of light, the electron charge and quantum mechanics. I would add here, and gravitation.

The number 137 is known as the "fine-structure constant", which is the probability factor controlling whether an electron will emit or absorb a photon. Experiments have shown this value to be around 137 but as there are no absolute boundaries, only fuzzy edges, when dealing with electronic fields, I would expect the value of 68.5 in relation to the magnetic monopole also to be in the fuzzy category. According to my research, I would make this value 68.50725813.

The fine-structure constant would therefore have a value of 137.0145162. This would make it possible to speculate.

I believe that the magnetic monopoles exist and that the creation of matter is dependent on the coupling of the poles into individual units. I can visualise streams of monopoles, both of positive and negative charge according to their spin, passing through each other and pairing off to form physical particles. The process would be much the same as the closing of a zipper. I described a similar process in the formation of the natural energy grid. The process would be complicated slightly by the fact that the monopoles would have respective anti-monopoles in a mirror-image reality, which manifests at a pulse rate tuned to the speed of light.

If the basic magnetic particle, or monopole, carries a charge that is 68.50725813 times greater than the electron, then we could expect the volume of the surrounding field to be directly related to this value. So, if we assume that the radius of the spherical field of the monopole is 68.50725813 units, then:

Volume of the monopole's spherical field:
(4 x 68.50725813 x 68.50725813 x 68.50725813 x 3.141592654)/3

$$= 1346785.298 \text{ cubic units}$$

To allow for the matter-antimatter cycle, we would then have to double this result:

1346785.298 x 2 $\qquad = 26935706$

The harmonic of 26935706 is equivalent to the value for 'E' in geometric Unified Equation 3, if the value for 'c' is equal to 143791.36438 minutes of arc per grid second (the harmonic reciprocal of gravity acceleration 6.95452056^{-5}). (See unified tables.)

If 'c' = 143791.36438, then '2c' = 287582.7286.

Calculation by harmonics:

$$E = \sqrt{[(2c + \sqrt{1/2}c) \times (2c)^2]}$$
$$= \sqrt{[(2875827286 + 5896829800) \times (82703825)]}$$
$$= \sqrt{(8772657086 \times 82703825)}$$
$$= \sqrt{7255323}$$
$$= 26935706 \text{ harmonic}$$

The Fine-Structure Constant:

It is said that Dr Edward Teller, the nuclear physicist who helped to develop the hydrogen bomb, derived a value for the fine-structure constant—or alpha, as it is known—from gravitation. Many well-known scientists have tried and failed to figure out how the magic number of alpha could be comfortably fitted into the quantum theory. One particular scientist spent many hours multiplying pi by a series of numbers hoping to come up with the value of alpha.

I found that if I divided my theoretical alpha by the constant phi multiplied by pi, I could get an interesting result:

$$137.0145162 \div (1618.034 \times 3.141592654)$$
$$= 137.0145162 \div 5083.203728$$
$$= 0.026954363 \text{ harmonic}$$

Could this be an accident? The harmonic 26954363 is the value for 'E' in Harmonic Unified Equation 3, if 'c' is equal to 143891.36438 minutes of arc per grid second (the speed of light in vacuum). (See unified tables.)

If 'c' = 143891.364919, then '2c' = 287782.7298.

Calculation by harmonics:
$$E = \sqrt{[(2c + \sqrt{1/2}c) \times (2c)^2]}$$
$$= \sqrt{[(2877827298 + 5894780400) \times (8281889957)]}$$
$$= \sqrt{(8772607698 \times 8281889957)}$$
$$= \sqrt{72653771590}$$
$$= 2695436358 \text{ harmonic.}$$

Chapter Three

INTERESTING ACTIVITY IN KAIPARA HARBOUR AUCKLAND, NEW ZEALAND

In late 1969 I was contacted by an engineer who worked for the Ministry of Works in Auckland. He had been told of a sighting I had had of an unidentified undersea object in the Kaipara Harbour area just north-west of Auckland city, and wanted to get some details of the incident from me. It was his intention to check the area. The sighting was made years before on 12th March 1965 and had caused some fuss with the Naval intelligence people when I had delayed reporting it for a short time. In those days I was a bit reluctant to let others know of my interest in any unidentified activity, be it on land, in the sky or water.

I gave the engineer the information he required and showed him the position as accurately as I could on an airways map. Shortly after this, on 5th September 1969, he investigated the area in a small boat and took some readings with a depth-sounder. He informed me later that as he was passing over the area at a speed of 7 knots with the depth-sounder indicating an average depth of 40 to 50 feet, the meter needle commenced to swing back and forth from 0 to 120 feet (the full extent of the range scale). The action was quite violent. This continued until he was abeam a position called black beacon. The meter then acted normally. He swung round and returned to the area and the meter reacted the same way. At the time the magnetic compass in the boat was stable.

It was from this position that all my investigations into the grid system and calculations commenced, and I know now that I would not have one fraction of the knowledge I have today if I had not made the flight that morning.

What I did not know until recently when the computer programs were available to convert normal latitude and longitude positions into their grid equivalents, was the mathematical association with the unified tables. It has taken over twenty years of hard work to understand what the geometric and mathematical relationships mean.

The engineer told me that a great hole had been discovered in the harbour-bed at the point of the disturbance, which indicated that my mysterious visitor had carried out some activity there. Whatever was left behind had an electronic imprint. The position he gave in his report was as near as he could get at:

Latitude 36° 29' 00" south / Longitude 174° 19' 15" east.

The latest conversion programs show a most likely position of:
Latitude 36° 29' 00.57603" south / Longitude 174° 19' 30.2344" east.

This is where the maximum disturbance should be.
When this is converted to grid latitude and longitude, the values are:
Latitude 33° 48' 15.53652" south / Longitude 72° 43' 02" west.

Grid harmonics are as follows:
Latitude 33.8043157 south:

56.1956843 - 33.8043157	= 22.3913686 (in 90° sector)
22.3913686 x 6 x 6 x 6	= 4836.535617
Square root of 4836.535617	= 69.54520556
Reciprocal	= 0.014379136
Harmonic	= 143791.36

The gravitational reciprocal 'speed' of light. (See unified tables.)
Longitude 72° 43' 02" west:

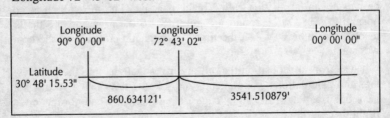

The great-circle distance of the Kaipara sighting position to longitude zero and longitude 90° (the calculated error would be ±50 feet).

3541.510879 - 860.634121	= 2680.876758 minutes of arc
Harmonic shift x 6 x 6 x 6 x 6	= 3474416.276
Multiplied by 2	= 6948832.552
Reciprocal	= 1.439090655^{-7}
Harmonic	= 143909.0655

The speed of light, electromagnetic.

The engineer continued to show an interest in my work and I had fairly close contact with him over a period of about eighteen months. He visited me at home several times and I went twice to his flat in Parnell, Auckland city. All other contacts were by phone, usually in the late evening. It became obvious after a while that he had access to far more information than I had and he passed small bits of data on to me from time to time in order to help me with my calculations. I did not have calculators or a computer to work with in those days, and he showed me how to work out great-circle tracks using mathematical formulae. It took me hours of work to get an answer to a problem which now takes a few minutes on the computer.

During one of his visits he handed me some maps of the Kaipara Harbour area which were copies of those used by the Ministry of Works. One was a general survey chart of the harbour showing soundings carried out by the Navy. This was useful in order to plot the position of the unidentified underwater object.

The other chart was far more interesting. It showed the method of construction and positioning of accelerographs to investigate the area for a North Auckland Nuclear Power Station. This was quite a surprise because I knew the public was not aware of this activity, and to this day I do not think there has been any mention to the public that such investigations have ever been carried out in New Zealand. Nuclear power is a very touchy subject in this country. The majority of New Zealanders do not want any of these stations constructed here. I would agree with this wholeheartedly, as I know without doubt that there are far safer means of generating electrical power. I still have these maps in safe keeping.

The accelerographs were positioned at Te Kawau Point and Oyster Point. I studied the maps again recently and wondered why they had positioned two accelerographs in the area. Maybe there was a geometric link between the two. I carried out some calculations on the computer and found that I could fit a set of unified harmonics very closely with the positions shown on the map. I agree that my calculations are only theoretical because no actual latitudes and longitudes are given on the Ministry map, but when the positions are transferred to a survey map, the close correlations look very suspicious.

The theoretical distance between the two instruments was 12.36506652 minutes of arc (nautical miles), and the track angle 309.9747404 degrees.

Harmonics of track angle:	= 309.9747404 degrees
	- 270.0000000
	= 39.9747404
39.9747404 x 6 x 6	= 1439.090655

This is a harmonic of 143909.0655 minutes of arc per grid second (electromagnetic).

Harmonics of distance	= 12.36506652 minutes
12.36506652 x 6	= 74.19039912
Divided by 2	= 37.09519956
Reciprocal	= **26957666** harmonic

The answer to Unified Equation 3 if 'c' is equal to 143909.0655.

The geometric positions of the accelerographs also indicated an association with unified harmonics within a very small margin of error. This could of course be coincidental, but the mathematical evidence strongly suggests otherwise.

I have often wondered over the years whether there is any intention of completing the project. Hopefully not.

The engineer continued making the occasional phone call to discuss various aspects of my research and showed particular interest in my knowledge of the methods used to detonate an atom bomb. I had discovered, quite by accident, that the geometric coordinates and mathematical values found in the grid system were applicable to atom bomb tests. I had a hunch that the unified equations I had discovered would have to be applied if the matter were to be disrupted. Einstein had stated that "the whole of our physical reality was manifested by the geometrics of space and time", so it was logical to assume that if we wished to destroy matter then a reverse geometric process would have to be set up. In other words, the relative motions of the atomic structure would have to be reversed at an instant of time to unlock the geometrics of the physical substance.

Thinking along these lines, I came to the conclusion that the relative motion between the Sun and the Earth at the critical time must have something to do with it, so I began to check the Sun position at the time of atom tests and found to my surprise that the geometric harmonics were evident at the time of detonation. The movement of the Sun in relation to a particular point on the Earth's surface was the final trigger for the bomb. The bomb was constructed geometrically. At the instant of detonation, the unstable matter within the bomb was imploded geometrically towards a central point—which guaranteed that a certain percentage of the material was moving in a certain direction—and the relative movement of the Sun-Earth relationship completed the combination of movements to make the atomic structure fly apart.

Also to complete the pattern, the bomb had to be set up on, over or below a certain geometric point on the Earth's surface.

This, of course, made it a bit difficult if you wished to wage a nuclear war. Each bomb would have to be programmed for a certain place and detonated at a certain time. Of course, your enemy would have the same problem and both sides could compute in advance the positions the enemy could hit. Stalemate. This problem was not a deterrent during the last world war when America destroyed Hiroshima and Nagasaki because they were the only ones who had constructed the atomic bombs. They had plenty of time to precalculate all the parameters necessary and make sure the bombs were dropped at the appropriate time. The Sun moved into position while the bombs were descending.

After I published all this there was a bit of a fuss, and I was contacted by various scientists and intelligence people.

The engineer asked me if I would precalculate a bomb test for him in order to prove the point. I was a bit reluctant as my knowledge of the process was very basic and I knew I had been lucky to get away with some calculations I had carried out for other government departments.

I had no idea of the number of geometric combinations that could be used to ensure an atomic detonation (and still do not to this day), so I could not be sure that any set of parameters that I came up with would be used for a particular test. I had cracked the secret but my knowledge was very limited. It was far easier to wait until a test had been carried out, then work backwards and find the geometric harmonics used by studying the Sun tables, time of detonation and the position of the bomb site, and work out the spherical triangle, formed by the combined information, on the Earth's surface.

The request from the engineer was therefore a real challenge, but to maintain my credibility I felt I had to at least try to come up with something.

The test, he told me, was to be held on Amchitka Island in the Aleutian chain during the next month or so. Could I work out the date and the time?

I spent about three hours that evening working out every combination that I could think of from a study of the Sun tables covering the next few weeks, and came up with only one possible time according to my limited knowledge. Well, go for broke, I thought, so I phoned him about 10.30 pm and passed on the information. He said he would contact me the next evening.

He called, as promised, and advised me that my calculations were not correct. I was obviously a bit disappointed but not too surprised, and said that I could not find any other date or time. If there were other possible times then I did not have the necessary knowledge to work them out. We left it at that.

Two days went by, then he called again. "You are right," he said. "If the bomb goes off, we will talk some more."

Three weeks went by, and at 22.00 hours GMT on 6th November 1971 the bomb went off. This was during the morning in New Zealand. I was one hour out in my calculation which was not too bad, I thought, considering the little I knew about the process. I knew the phone had to ring and I waited expectantly all day.

At about 7.30 pm the call came. He congratulated me on the effort but seemed a little hesitant on what to say next.

I chuckled and said, "You have a problem."

"What makes you say that?" he asked.

I replied, "Well, I believe that you have to offer me a job."

"What makes you think that? Do you know who I am?"

"I believe that you are working for some intelligence group, possibly the CIA."

He had a slight American or Canadian accent and it was obvious he had contact with top people overseas. He had shown me radio gear in his flat and said he had contact with many stations around the world. Also, the bits and pieces of information he had passed on to me over the months indicated without doubt that he was involved in some of the secret work going on.

He admitted that he worked for the CIA and that, yes, there was a job offer.

I asked where I would be working, for whom I would be working, what I would be doing, and how much they were going to pay me.

None of these questions could be answered, he said, unless I said yes to the offer.

All he could say was that if I worked for them, my family and I would never want for material things for the rest of our lives.

I asked for time to think and spent the next two days mulling it over. It was very tempting.

This was the type of work I really wished to be involved in. But all the negative sides to the offer put a damper on things. I realised that they did not want me for my knowledge. What I knew was kindergarten stuff compared to the scientists involved.

The main reason they wanted me was to shut me up. Probably put me in some out-of-the-way place and give me a boring and menial job to do and pin me down with the secrets act. Plenty of money and no real future for myself and family.

I contacted him and told him no.

To my surprise, he patted me on the back for my decision. I asked him why he thought that way and, if he was not happy about being involved himself, why he didn't get out.

He indicated that the penalties would be too great. He was involved for good. But he doesn't have to worry now, having passed away a few years ago. He was a very likeable guy and we got on very well during our months of contact.

Shortly after this, I contacted the Security Intelligence Service and told them what had gone on over the months and the reasons why I had turned the offer down—one being that I had a hunch I might be committing treason if I worked secretly for a foreign government. Evidently this could have been so.

I have not worried much about atom bomb tests since that time. I wrote about the geometric make-up of the bomb and the necessary geometric parameters for detonation in my earlier books, but nobody believed it.

It is obvious, if what I say is true, that an all-out nuclear war is completely illogical and highly improbable. Now that several countries have the secret, it is a stand-off. Conventional weapons are so advanced now—they do the job just as well and are far cheaper.

Hopefully the public will wake up one day and realise they are being conned.

Chapter Four

THE HARMONICS OF HIROSHIMA AND NAGASAKI

It was 1971 when I first published the fact that atomic bombs were geometric devices that had to be detonated on specific geometric positions, and that the timing of the detonations had to be calculated with extreme accuracy. The process was directly related to the geometrics of the Earth and Sun positions. The problem is that of relative motion in space, and the Earth-Sun positions create the final trigger to unlock the atomic structure. Einstein laid down the rules when he stated that, "all physical reality is manifested by the geometrics of space and time". It follows, logically, that to disrupt matter we have to arrange a geometric system that will reverse this process.

When an atomic device is detonated on a fixed point at a testing ground, the calculations are relatively easy but if a bomb is to be dropped from an aircraft, the problems of geometric position and accurate timing become much more difficult.

It amazes me that after all these years no one has asked the question, "What about Hiroshima and Nagasaki?" If the timing had to be so accurate, just how was it possible to drop the bomb from an aircraft and have a successful explosion? The answers to this are on public record. For months before the bomb drops, the especially-picked aircrews carried out intensive training and practised dropping dummy bombs into three-hundred-foot-diameter circles from high altitude with split-second timing. They became very skilled at hitting the target within the 150-foot radius margin of error. This is probably close to the maximum allowable error in order to guarantee a successful detonation.

The truth is that an atomic bomb has to be released from the aircraft at a precalculated split second of time so that when the device has reached the planned altitude for detonation, the Sun has moved into the required position relative to the Earth's surface to complete the combination of relative motions necessary to disrupt the geometrics of the atomic structures within the critical mass.

A possible hint that accurate timing is essential for a bomb drop may be found in what is said to be "the crazy, hit-and-miss story of why the bomb was dropped on Nagasaki". The only person who was on both bombing missions over Japan was Jacob Beser. During an interview with the *Washington Post Weekly*, he said that the drop on Nagasaki actually missed the target. According to him they intended to bomb the residential area of the city, but in fact the bomb exploded at the far end over the Mitsubishi Heavy Industries Arsenal.

The activity before the bomb was dropped was also most unusual. The primary target, according to the official records, was the city of Kokura, but when the aircraft arrived overhead it was smoked and hazed in and, although they were said to have possible fuel problems, they circled around for over an hour before they proceeded to the secondary target, Nagasaki. During this time of apparent indecision, Japanese fighter aircraft were trying to reach them at their high altitude in order to shoot them down.

Many other excuses were made for the apparent error in the detonation point and the delay in getting the job done, but I believe that the answers are quite straightforward:

(1) The bomb was not dropped off target. Within a small margin of error it was positioned right where they wanted it to be. Calculations now indicate this, as demonstrated.

(2) There was no indecision while the aircraft was apparently in aimless flight around the Kokura area. They had to wait until the geometric relationship between the Sun position and the target point was viable for a successful detonation.

It was only in recent years that I was able to get hold of the information necessary to calculate the relationship of the Sun positions and the epicentres of the Hiroshima and Nagasaki explosions. A contact in the United States sent me computer copies of all the times, dates, detonation sites and Sun positions, from the first test at Alamagord up to 1985. The following are those for Hiroshima and Nagasaki respectively.

Date GMT	Time GMT	Latitude	Longitude	Sun GHA	Sun DEC.
5 Aug 45	23.266666	34.3913888°N	132.458055°E	167.53758	16.90122°N
9 Aug 45	2.033333	32.7701°N	129.865622°E	209.12833	16.01111°N

Diagram 5

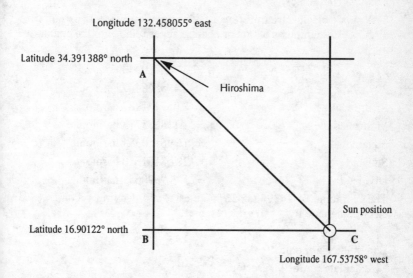

Longitude 132.458055° east

Latitude 34.391388° north

A

Hiroshima

Sun position

Latitude 16.90122° north

B   C

Longitude 167.53758° west

From this data we can now re-calculate the geometric coordinates for the two wartime bomb-drops.

Actual values given for the detonation point and the Sun position.

The distances between points are calculated as sections of great circles.

HIROSHIMA

First of all we will analyse the harmonic values of the detonation point. It would have been a miracle if the bomb-aimer had been able to place the bomb exactly on the previously calculated point from such a high altitude, so we can assume a slight error within the 150-foot allowable radius from dead centre. Computer calculations indicate that the error was in fact approximately 111 feet in latitude and 104 feet in longitude.

The calculated position for detonation:
Latitude 34.391697° north / Longitude 132.45840768° east.

Latitude Harmonics:
The small-circle circumference of latitude 34.391697° is equal to 17,824.21975 minutes of arc, or nautical miles relative to the equator.

21,600 - 17,824.21975	= 3775.78025 minutes of arc
3775.78025 ÷ 6 ÷ 6 ÷ 6 ÷ 6 ÷ 6	= 0.485568447 harmonic
Reciprocal	= 2.059441887 harmonic
Multiplied by 2	= 4.118883773 harmonic
Squared	= 16.96520354 harmonic
Squared	= 287.8181310 harmonic
Divided by 2	= 143.9090655 harmonic

The harmonic of **143909.0655** minutes of arc per grid second. (See electromagnetic light and gravity tables.)

Longitude Harmonics:
To calculate for the 90° sector:

132.4584076 - 90	= 42.4584076°
90 - 42.4584076	= 47.5415924°
47.5415924 - 42.4584076	= 5.08318480°
Divided by 6	= 0.847197466 harmonic
Multiplied by 2	= 1.694394933 harmonic
Squared	= 2.870974190 harmonic
Divided by 2	= **1.435487095** harmonic

This would be the harmonic of the actual speed of light at that latitude: 143548.7 minutes of arc per grid second.

This can be calculated very accurately by the world grid computer program we now have on the market. (Also see the light and gravity tables for interpolation.)

From this we can see that Hiroshima was obviously a viable position for the detonation of an atomic device.

The latitude displacement (A - B) between the detonation point and the Sun position was calculated to be:

	17.4901688°
	= 1049.410128 minutes
21,600 - 1,049.410128	= 20550.58987 minutes
20550.58987 - 1049.410128	= 19501.17974 minutes
19501.17974 ÷6÷6÷6÷6÷6÷6÷6	= 0.069662993 harmonic
Reciprocal	= **14.35482385** harmonic

Again, we have a harmonic which is within a minute fraction of the actual speed of light value of 143548.7 minutes of arc per grid second at the detonation point. (See tables.)

Longitudinal displacement of the detonation point and the Sun position (B - C):

Allowing for a one-second error in the given detonation time, the great-circle distance (actual), (B - C), would be:

	3430.252471 minutes of arc
3430.252471 x 6	= 20581.51483 harmonic
Multiplied by 2	= 41163.02965 harmonic
Squared	= 1694395010 harmonic
Squared	= 2870974450 harmonic
Divided by 2	= 1.43548722^{18} harmonic

We have, again, the harmonic of the actual speed of light at the detonation point: 143548.7 minutes of arc per grid second. (See tables.)

The final harmonic, allowing for the one-second error in the detonation time, would be created by the great-circle distance between the detonation point and the Sun position, (A - C):

	3361.1253 minutes of arc
3361.1253 x 6 x 6 x 6	= 726003.0648 harmonic
The square root	= **269.4444**

This is the harmonic result derived from Unified Equation 3 when the speed of light is reduced by the harmonic of phi, or 1618.034. (See mathematics of the grid.)

All in all, an excellent set of results, allowing for the maximum error of 111 feet in the detonation point and one second in given time.

NAGASAKI

To initiate an atomic explosion, the critical mass of the bomb material has to be assembled very quickly so that it does not blow apart before the atomic reaction has been completed. Uranium-235 had been used for the Hiroshima bomb and a gun-type device was used to bring the segments of uranium together to complete the required spherical mass.

The Nagasaki bomb was of a different type. Plutonium was used to create the critical mass and it had been found by experiment that the gun-type method used to assemble the material was not fast enough to stop premature detonation. A new method was therefore designed which consisted of shaped charges arranged in a spherical pattern around an inner hollow sphere of plutonium. When the charges were simultaneously detonated, the resulting implosion squeezed the hollow plutonium sphere into a dense critical mass at such high speed that an atomic reaction was guaranteed to take place.

Both methods, of course, depended on the geometric placing of the device on the Earth's surface.

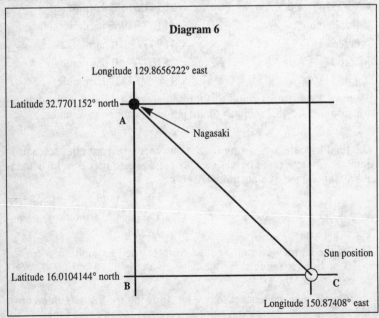

Diagram 6

Longitude 129.8656222° east

Latitude 32.7701152° north — A

Nagasaki

Sun position

Latitude 16.0104144° north — B   C

Longitude 150.87408° east

Because of this difference in geometrics, it was more difficult for me to calculate the most likely set of coordinates used to explode the plutonium core. I spent many hours on the computer and finally came to the conclusion that the bomb was almost perfectly placed on the target. The timing for the Sun position appeared to be about one second in error. The following geometric pattern was evident:

Location of detonation point: Latitude 32.770152° north.

The geometric harmonics associated with this position formed an unusual combination. I had discovered, during other research, that curved and straight-line coordinates were sometimes used in the positioning of certain scientific projects. When I was finding it difficult to calculate accurate harmonics for the given Nagasaki detonation point, I decided to try the combination of curved and straight-line coordinates between the equator and Nagasaki—one coordinate being the great circle or curved distance over the surface of the Earth, and the other, the direct chord distance between the points. A fractional change in the latitude value gave the following results, an error of 18.72 geodetic feet off target.

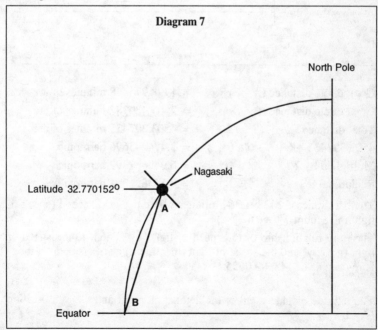

Diagram 7

North Pole

Nagasaki

Latitude 32.770152°

A

B

Equator

Great circle distance (A - B)	= 1966.20912 minutes of arc
Direct chord distance (A - B)	= <u>1939.518767</u> minutes of arc
Difference	= 26.690367 minutes of arc
$26.690367 \div 6 \div 6 \div 6 \div 6$	= 0.020594418 harmonic
Multiplied by 2	= 0.041188837 harmonic
Squared	= 1.6965203^{-3} harmonic
Squared	= 2.8781813^{-6} harmonic
Divided by 2	= <u>1.439090655</u> harmonic

The harmonic of the electromagnetic speed of light, 143909.0655 minutes of arc per grid second. (See tables.)

Detonation point: Longitude 129.8656222° east.

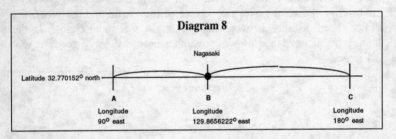

Diagram 8

Nagasaki

Latitude 32.770152° north

A — Longitude 90° east
B — Longitude 129.8656222° east
C — Longitude 180° east

Great circle distance (A - B)	= 1998.976448 minutes of arc
Great circle distance (B - C)	= <u>2504.420987</u> minutes of arc
Total distance	= 4503.397435 minutes of arc
$4503.397435 \div 6 \div 6 \div 6 \div 6$	= 3.474843696 harmonic
Multiplied by 2	= 6.949687392 harmonic
Reciprocal	= **0.143891364** harmonic

The harmonic of 143891.364 minutes of arc per grid second (speed of light in vacuum). (See tables.)

The ratio relationship of the speed of light in vacuum to the speed of light (gravity) and the speed of light (maximum) also sets up a harmonic resonance of 143909.0655.

The latitude displacement of the detonation point and the Sun position (A - B):

A - B	= 1005.581133 minutes of arc
21600 - 1005.581133	= 20594.41887 minutes of arc
Multiplied by 2	= 41188.83774 harmonic
Squared	= 16965203540 harmonic
Squared	= 2.8781813^{18} harmonic
Divided by 2	= **1.439090655** harmonic

The harmonic of 143909.0655 minutes of arc per grid second (electro-magnetic).

The longitude displacement between the detonation point and the Sun position, (B - C):

B - C	= 150.8740888 - 129.8656222
	= 21.0084666
$21.0084666 \div 6 \div 6 \div 6 \div 6 \div 6 \div 6 \div 6 \div 6 \div 6$	
	= 3.4744162^{-7} harmonic
Multiplied by 2	= 6.9488325^{-7} harmonic
Reciprocal	= 1439090.655

The harmonic of 143909.0655 minutes of arc per grid second (electro-magnetic).

The displacement between the detonation point and the Sun position. (A - C):

Displacement (great circle)	= 1520.305 mins of arc (± 60 feet)
Displacement (chord distance)	= <u>1507.946375</u> minutes of arc
The difference	= 12.358625 minutes of arc
$12.358625 \div 60$	= 0.205977083 degrees
Multiplied by 2	= 0.411954166 harmonic
Squared	= 0.169706235 harmonic
Squared	= 0.0288 harmonic

This is the harmonic of 288000, twice the maximum speed of light of 144000 minutes of arc per grid second (relative to the Earth's surface).

There does not appear to be any doubt that the Nagasaki bomb was dropped almost right on target, with pinpoint accuracy. A remarkable feat under the circumstances.

An all-out atomic war would be a cumbersome exercise under these geometric conditions. Breeder stations that produce the atomic material for the manufacture of bombs also require placement on a geometric position, according to the evidence. This would make the checking of any other countries wanting to get into the game fairly easy.

Chapter Five

ARE MYSTERIOUS EXPLOSIONS THE RESULT OF SECRET RESEARCH?

My first book, *Harmonic 33*, published in 1968, described a number of massive explosions which occurred in the Auckland city area, a major city in the north island of New Zealand. Two of these reported as follows:

22 March 1957:

"City Explosion Puzzle For Police

An extensive police search failed to find the source of a violent explosion which rocked the central police station and nearby buildings in Wellesley and Rutland streets at about 10 o'clock last night.

Mr T. J. Burrows of 8 Ferncroft Street, Grafton, was passing the Seddon Memorial College when the explosion occurred. He described it as "a muffled kind of explosion which shook the pavement and seemed to come from inside the building".

In the belief that a large safe had been blown, detectives and uniformed police searched the College and the offices of the education board. The College engineering workshops and a number of other premises were also inspected.

Constable P. Wiseman with others, saw a flash from the upstairs window of the Central Police Station, followed by the percussion of an explosion which was heard as far away as the Auckland Hospital.

The weather office rules out the possibility that the noise came from an isolated thunderclap. Some thought it may have been caused by a fireball."

23 September 1966:

"City Shocked Awake as Explosion Rips Factory

Thousands of Aucklanders were awakened at 4 am today by a massive explosion which tore apart a foundry at Rosebank Road, Avondale, and caused widespread damage to adjoining buildings.

No one was injured in the explosion, but one family, whose house about 60 yards away from the blast was lifted from its foundations, said everything "lit up like day" as glass showered into the house from blown windows.

The blast, which was heard as far away as Waiuku, 27 miles away, ripped 30-feet-long sheets of roofing iron from their supports and tossed them into twisted heaps on neighbouring gardens up to 100 yards away. It snapped heavy steel reinforcing beams supporting the foundry roof and tore concrete blocks from the foundry walls and threw them into gardens."

The report continued with a general description of the damage, then followed on with an interview with Mr E. C. Knibbs, the owner of the house immediately next door to the factory. The wooden house, which was lifted from its foundations, also had its roof cracked and almost every window broken.

Mr and Mrs Knibbs said they were first awakened by a muffled crump, like a bomb explosion in the distance, followed by an extremely loud crack like a monster firework. The house shook and rolled and all the windows blew in, showering the house with glass. After the initial shock, they climbed out of bed and peered through the window which overlooked the factory next door. They found that most of it had disintegrated and that they could see right through the wrecked structure.

The sight that confronted them was most unusual. A thin pencil of light extended vertically from the floor level of the factory, where a hole was later found, to about roof-level. This beam of light was clearly defined without any fuzzy edges, and was of a brilliant colour. Both Mr and Mrs Knibbs had great difficulty describing the exact colour and both said it was like a flame of an acetylene welding torch, with brilliant red, orange and yellow all mixed up together.

As they watched, the beam slowly disappeared from roof level to the floor as if it were descending into the ground, and as it reached the floor a small dome of light or ball of fire formed and quickly spread. In less than a minute this section of the factory was ablaze.

The reports have been condensed somewhat from the original accounts in my book, but the main interest in these two particular explosions at the time was that they had taken place on energy grid lines and that they were right on 288 seconds apart—this being twice the speed-of-light harmonic shown in other sections of this book. Not only that, the two explosions were equidistant from a secret American research base at Kauri Point on the north shore of Auckland city. The geometric pattern formed a perfect isosceles triangle. Other interesting geometric relationships were associated with this base and were pointed out at the time and shown on a map of Auckland. The one thing I did not check until years later was the time interval between the two explosions.

Now that I have far more background knowledge to work with, I have been looking over previous research data and filling in gaps which were not obvious during my early attempts to find out what the scientists were up to. I suddenly had a hunch that the time factor should be considered on some of this activity and decided to check the

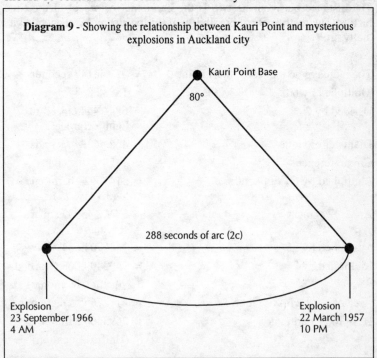

Diagram 9 - Showing the relationship between Kauri Point and mysterious explosions in Auckland city

Kauri Point Base

80°

288 seconds of arc (2c)

Explosion
23 September 1966
4 AM

Explosion
22 March 1957
10 PM

interval between the explosion in the city and the one at Rosebank Road. The results were quite startling.

The interval, surprisingly, came to 3472 days, which is the harmonic reciprocal of 288, the displacement of the two explosions (288 seconds of arc). The mathematical possibility of this occurring by chance is virtually nil. I believe that it is almost certain that the scientists were carrying out some sort of experiment in space-time which required a geometric pattern to be set up in the Auckland area. No one was injured, but the resulting damage proved it to be a very costly exercise.

Time difference between explosions	= 3472 days
Distance between explosion points	= 288 seconds of arc
Reciprocal of 288	= 0.003472 harmonic

It appears obvious that the explosions were not caused by accident. The distance between the two is the harmonic reciprocal of the time factor. The mathematical possibility of this occurring by chance is virtually nil.

The radius of action from Kauri Point	= 231.48147 seconds
Multiplied by 60	= 13888.888
Divided by 2	= 6944.444 (speed-of-light reciprocal)
Diameter of circle	= 462.96294 seconds
Circumference	= 1454.441 seconds
Multiplied by 60 x 60 x 60	= 31415927 harmonic of pi (3.1415927)
Area of segment	= 37408.45932 square seconds
Multiplied by 36	= 1346704.534
Multiplied by 2	= 2693409.068 (Unified Equation harmonic)
Area of Earth cross-section	= 37127665 square mins
Reciprocal harmonic	= 2693409 harmonic (Unified Equation)

Chapter Six

HARMONIC TRANSMISSION AND RECEIVING

I have been aware for many years now that scientists have been carrying out gravitational and other types of electromagnetic research in a number of countries around the world. I realise, of course, that the knowledge that I have discovered to date regarding the unification of these forces is only a fraction of that held by the various scientific groups. I have had to put together all the material at hand, piece by piece, from the information gathered from the study of UFO activity, while they have had access to data that has been available from historical times and held to the present day by secret organisations.

Because of this awareness, I often carry out a computer check of positions where unusual activity has occurred or where technical activity is being carried out in unusual places. This has now become a routine exercise and I have found that there is a general pattern of harmonic associations to look for. The computer program compiled by Rod Maupin and I now makes the exercise much easier, and if the position under study falls on a harmonic site it usually shows up fairly quickly. The harmonic values can be processed in a similar way each time, and it is this repetition of method and the correlation with the established unified tables that indicates the probability that a comparatively small group of people are aware of a new and advanced technology.

I do not see this as any great problem as advanced research must be carried out to ensure scientific progress, but I believe that we have the right to know of the activity and also the right to have some say in how the knowledge is used.

One of the places of interest that caught my attention was a large communication station established on the north island of New Zealand.

At a given cost of NZ$1.39 million, a signal intelligence high-frequency direction-finding station was constructed on 25 hectares of land near a small west coast settlement called Tangimoana. Opened by the Prime Minister on 18th August 1982, it was said at the time that the station would significantly improve defence communications in New Zealand and that it also could be used for search and rescue purposes.

There is certainly nothing sinister about the complex and there is no question that installations such as this are necessary in case they are needed for the mutual defence of our country and that of our allies.

As a purely theoretical exercise, I decided to feed the position of the station into the computer to see what came up, and the first rough results I had were passed on to the appropriate authorities to see if they wished to make a comment. No particular interest was shown regarding my calculations at the time.

Since then I have made a more comprehensive check of the position using the grid computer program and have obtained quite a satisfactory series of unified harmonic values. This, no doubt, will be put down to chance but I found the exercise most interesting.

The theoretical position calculated by the computer which should give the best results for transmission, according to my present findings, is:

Latitude 40° 19' 07.878" south / Longitude 175° 14' 35.7" east.

The analysis of these values follows:

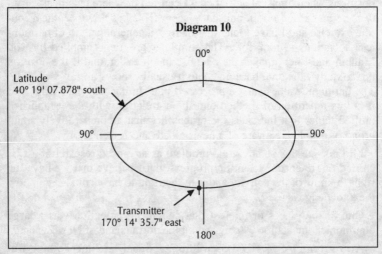

Diagram 10

00°

Latitude
40° 19' 07.878" south

90° — | — 90°

Transmitter
170° 14' 35.7" east

180°

Latitude 40° 19' 07.878" south:

Each 90° sector is equal to 4117.259375 minutes of arc (nautical miles).

If we calculate the circumference at this parallel of latitude in minutes of arc relative to the equator, we have:

$$16469.0375 \text{ minutes}$$
$$\text{(or nautical miles)}$$

Therefore, each sector of 90°	= 4117.259375 minutes of arc
This value squared	= 16951824.76
This value squared	= 2.8736436^{14}
Divided by 2	= 1.436821849^{14}
Harmonically	= 143682.1849

The speed of light, geometric, at this latitude.

If we now check the gravitational and light tables, we see that the value for the speed of light, geometric (actual), is also 143682.1849 (143682.2) for this latitude, which shows quite clearly that the given position and the theoretical tables match very accurately. The computer programs calculate these values for any latitude.

Furthermore, if we subtract the true speed-of-light value for that latitude from the speed of light, maximum, of 144000 minutes of arc per grid second, we can calculate the following:

$$\begin{array}{r} 144000.0000 \\ - \underline{143682.1849} \\ \underline{317.8151} \end{array}$$

If we now shift this value up the harmonic scale by the multiplication of 6:

317.8151 x 6 x 6 x 6 x 6	= 411888.3696
Squared	= 1.6965202^{11}
Squared	= 2.878181^{22}
Divided by 2	= 1.439090655^{22}
Equivalent speed-of-light harmonic	= 143909.0655 minutes of arc per grid second

As shown in other sections of this book, if this value for the speed of light is used in Unified Equation 2, then:

$$E = (2c + \sqrt{(1/2c)})(2c)^2$$
$$= (287818.131 + \sqrt{(1/287818.131)})(287818.131)^2$$

Harmonics $\quad = (287818131 + 186397860)(82839276)$
$$= 474215991 \times 82839276$$
$$= 3928371 \text{ harmonic}$$

This harmonic of 3928371 is directly associated with the Earth's magnetic field and is also the reciprocal of the value 2545.5844 minutes of arc built into the polar segments of the energy grid.

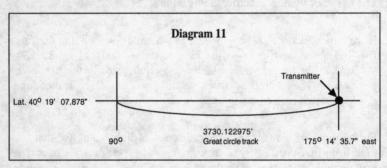

Diagram 11

Transmitter

Lat. 40° 19' 07.878"

90°

3730.122975'
Great circle track

175° 14' 35.7" east

Longitude 175° 14' 35.7" east:

The harmonics connected with the longitudinal position of the aerial system can be calculated by checking the great-circle displacement within the associated 90-degree sector at latitude 40° 19' 07.878" south.

The great-circle distance between 90° east and 175° 14' 35.7" east proved to be: $\qquad$ 3730.122975 minutes of arc

If we shift this value down the harmonic scale by the division of 6, we have:

$3730.122975 \div 6 \div 6 \div 6 \qquad = 287181305$ harmonic
Divided by 2 $\qquad = 1439090655$ harmonic

Equivalent speed-of-light harmonic = 143909.0655 minutes of arc per grid second

So we see that both the latitude and longitude positions have mathematical affiliations with this particular speed-of-light value.

A description of the circular aerial array of the direction-finding station was given in a magazine article I read some years ago. It is said that it consists of a ring of aluminium aerials 150 metres in diameter, with an outer circle of 48 poles, 12 metres high, and capable of monitoring the lower half of the high frequency band, 2 MHz to 15 MHz.

Diagram 12 - Showing the Ground Plan of the Transmitter-Receiver.

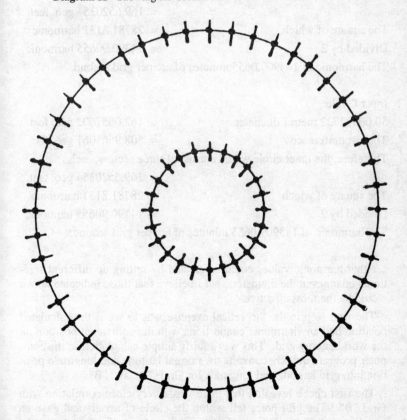

Concentrically within the larger circle is a 50-metre-diameter circle of 24 antennas, each 6 metres high, which would monitor the upper part of the high-frequency band up to 30 MHz.

If we alter these values fractionally to 150.0144817 metres and 50.00482722 metres respectively, then the following unified values can be derived:

Outer Circle:

150.0144817 metres diameter	= 486.0172806 geo. feet
The circumference	= 1526.868318 geo. feet

Therefore, the outer circle would consist of nine sectors, each

	= 169.6520354 geo. feet
The square of which	= 28781.8131 harmonic
Divided by 2	= 14390.90655 harmonic

The harmonic of 143909.0655 minutes of arc per grid second.

Inner Circle:

50.00482722 metres diameter	= 162.0057602 geo. feet
The circumference	= 508.9561061 geo. feet

Therefore, the inner circle would consist of three sectors, each

	= 169.6520354 geo. feet
The square of which	= 28781.8131 harmonic
Divided by 2	= 14390.90655 harmonic

The harmonic of 143909.0655 minutes of arc per grid second.

Other harmonic values could be created by setting up different fractional changes in the diameters, but I believe that those indicated above would be the most effective.

The next step in the theoretical exercise was to see if the calculated position had any harmonic connections with the equivalent position on the world energy grid. This was a fairly simple calculation as the computer program quickly converts the normal latitude and longitude position into grid latitude and longitude for Grids "A" and "B".

The first check revealed that there was a very close correlation with Grid "B". The grid point fell within the circle of aerials and gave an excellent set of harmonics. After a further series of calculations, the closest position to the centre of the aerial circles was found to be:

Latitude 40° 19' 07.4466" south / Longitude 175° 14' 37.73" east.

This was equivalent to a Grid "B" position of:

Grid latitude 37° 20' 56.8932" south /

Grid longitude 70° 42' 38.44" west, or

Latitude 37.349137° south / Longitude 70.710677867° west.

The harmonics of the latitude:

The circumference of the parallel of grid latitude, 37.349137 degrees, in minutes of arc relative to the grid equator, is:

> 17170.99538 minutes of arc or nautical miles

The circumference of the grid equator:

> 21600 minutes of arc or nautical miles

The difference:	21600.00000
	- 17170.99538
	4429.00462
17170.99538 - 4429.00462	= 12741.99076
12741.99076 ÷ 6 ÷ 6 ÷ 6	= 58.99069793
Reciprocal	= 0.016951825
Squared	= 2.873643700^{-4}
Divided by 2	= 1.436821800^{-4}
The harmonic	= 143682.18

It is evident that the grid latitude has a harmonic affinity with the actual speed-of-light factor 143682.18, shown to be related to the aerial position in the previous calculations.

The harmonics of the longitude:

The harmonic relationship of the grid longitude was quite easily calculated by moving the value up the scale by multiplication of the 6 increment:

70.710677867 x 6 x 6　　　　　　　　　= 2545.5844

Harmonics 2545.5844 and the reciprocal 3.928371^{-4} were previously shown to be related to the Earth's magnetic field and the positioning of aerial-type objects around the north and south grid poles.

The Grid "B" position falls between the calculated positions of the inner and outer circles of the aerial array, which is almost a perfect match considering the fractional errors which must exist in the calculations. I was quite happy with the results.

Could it be that the theoretical exercise is showing positive answers? Other places have been checked and they also show similar results. Are they also mathematical accidents?

The Washington Link

The early 1980s saw great public concern in New Zealand about the proposed construction of an observatory not far from the small township of Blenheim on the south island. It would be what is termed a "transit circle observing station" that would be used to determine the positions and motions of the stars. It was said that the station would have direct links with the United States Naval Observatory in Washington, DC.

The main concern at the time was that the station would have links with the military and could be used for the accurate guidance of nuclear missiles. This did not go down well with the public as New Zealand had been declared a nuclear-free zone.

The debate went on for a number of years but eventually the station was built at Waihopai and has been in operation since 1989. The large satellite receiving dish is supposedly set up to monitor communications in the Pacific area for domestic reasons and trade security.

The public fuss died down and there was very little in the media about the station until November 1993 when an article appeared in the local papers. A Naval intelligence document had come to light which was said to have "great significance" in the debate over Waihopai and Tangimoana's signal intelligence activities. The claims that the Tangimoana communications station and the Waihopai satellite dish were built to collect military intelligence information for the United States appeared to be correct.

The document stated that the United States National Security Agency controlled all signal intelligence collected from the reporting sites and "second-party producers". The second parties are listed as the United Kingdom, Canada, Australia and New Zealand. The activity was said to be largely beyond government control.

More information can be gleaned from the media files for those interested, but my attention was focussed on the probability that there was some close connection between Tangimoana and Waihopai facilities besides the gathering of intelligence. Could there be a geometric link-up based on the unified values which have become apparent in my research? It was a simple operation to compute the distance, in minutes of arc, between the two stations and compare the results with the tables.

The approximate centre of the small parcel of land upon which the Waihopai satellite dish was constructed was given by the Department of Survey and Land Information as:

Latitude 41° 34' 42" south / Longitude 173° 44' 23" east.

The latitude value was of immediate interest. The actual speed or acceleration of light at that latitude according to the unified computer tables, is 143556.632 minutes of arc per grid second.

144000 - 143556.632	= 443.368
Multiplied by 6 harmonic 14 times	= 3.4744162^{13} harmonic
Multiplied by 2	= 6.948832513^{13} harmonic
Reciprocal	= 1.439090655^{-14} harmonic

The harmonic of 143909.0655 minutes of arc per grid second (electromagnetic).

The distance to the Tangimoana position calculated at:
Latitude 40° 19' 07.878" south / Longitude 175° 14' 35.7" east.

Was	= 101.7472955587 minutes of arc
	= 1.695788259 degrees

Only a fractional correction of approximately 13.6 feet was necessary to give a harmonic value of:

	1.695825547 degrees
Squared:	= 2.875824285 harmonic
Divided by 2	= 1.437912142 harmonic

The harmonic of 143791.214 minutes of arc per grid second. (See the gravity reciprocal value for electromagnetic transmission, Table 3.)

Other harmonic values were also evident in the full geometric pattern between the two points. Extremely small errors were there but I consider the values to be too close to be chance. The communications systems were geometrically connected, possibly for some other scientific purpose yet to be discovered.

Chapter Seven

THE LINK BETWEEN HUMAN BRAINWAVES, THE CAVITY RESONANCE BETWEEN THE EARTH AND THE IONOSPHERE, AND GRAVITY

In my earlier works I have shown that the human body is linked harmonically to its natural environment due to its gestation period, blood heat, major acupuncture points and the geometrics of the DNA spiral. It seems that we are tuned in varying degrees—some more so than others—to our natural surroundings which affect our day-to-day well-being. Theoretically, those who have near-perfect harmonic resonance with all these factors would be the most healthy. All the cells in the body would be in almost perfect rhythm and function at peak efficiency. There would be a very small percentage of people in the world lucky enough to be in this group.

Unfortunately, the vast majority of us go through our lives accepting that we must contend with an average health record and varying degrees of success in our endeavours because of this. Some of the main causes for the breakdown in the cell structure of the human body in modern times would be the worldwide pollution of our environment and the background of natural and man-made radiation that we are forced to live in. Hopefully we will be able to eradicate some of these causes in the future.

Recently, some more facts have come to my attention which reinforce the theory that the human body has a natural affinity with particular Earth harmonic rhythms. The human brain functions within a distinct range of electromagnetic wave patterns. The general groupings come under the headings of Delta, Theta, Alpha and Beta.

The frequency ranges are:

Delta:	0.02 - 3 hertz
Theta:	3 - 7 hertz
Alpha:	7 - 13.5 hertz
Beta:	13.5 - 27 hertz

During sleep or unconsciousness, the waves are in the Delta group. The dream state is said to be in the Theta group. When a person is awake and fully aware of his or her surroundings, the wave frequencies are found in the Beta range.

When the individual is in a wakeful state but completely relaxed, the brainwaves produced are in the Alpha group. It has been discovered that the majority of waves produced in this state are those of 10.6 Hz.

According to the unified theory, a more accurate value for the dominant transmission of 10.6 Hz would be 10.598084 Hz. Calculations indicate that the Alpha baseline frequency has a direct harmonic link with the gravitational values demonstrated in the unified tables. Considering the fact that the gravitational harmonics are the basis for the whole of our reality, it should not be surprising to find that the human mind has an affinity for this basic frequency.

The cavity resonance between the Earth's surface and the ionosphere which manifests in ELF (extra low frequency) wave-trains, can also be linked with human brain activity. The surface of the Earth and the ionosphere form a wave-guide which channels the ELF waves, produced by lightning strikes, in a circular path around the world. This is known as the "Schumann resonance". Dr W. O. Schumann was the first to carry out experiments in this area, and in collaboration with Dr H. Konig in Germany he developed the electronic equipment necessary for the verification of the phenomenon.

It was discovered that the average frequency range of the waves was 7 to 13.5 Hz. But the most startling fact was that the wave-trains that occurred most frequently were those of 10.6 Hz—the Alpha brainwave pattern produced most frequently by the relaxed human being. The Alpha brainwaves and ELF waves are so similar that it is sometimes hard to tell them apart during some experiments.

It seems that we are walking radio transmitters, tuned into our surrounding environment. Could this have some bearing on the psychic abilities of some individuals and the possibility of telepathic communication?

If, instead of 10.6 Hz, we assume the true value of 10.598084 Hz, then:

(10.598084 x 8) ÷ 9	= 9.4205193 cycles per grid second
9.4205193 x 6 x 6 x 6 x 6 x 6 x 6 x 6	= 26371424 harmonic
This value squared	= 69545205 harmonic
Reciprocal	= 143791364 harmonic

It will be seen that the harmonic values are those of gravity, 143791.364, demonstrated in the unified tables.

This would also be a good place to point out that the Earth is said to have a natural frequency of 7.82 Hz. This has been published in many articles over the last few years but I have not seen any reference to this in any scientific journal. If any reader can find such a reference and send it on to me, I would be very grateful. I believe that the value would be very close to correct, because if we convert it into grid time we can get the following harmonics:

(7.8174366 x 8) ÷ 9	= 69488325 harmonic
The reciprocal	= 143909.0655 harmonic

Grid speed of light, electromagnetic.

(7.8200534 x 8) ÷ 9	= 69511586 harmonic
Reciprocal	= 143860.909 harmonic

Grid speed of light, in air.

(7.8238356 x 8) ÷ 9	= 69545205 harmonic
Reciprocal	= 143791.364 harmonic

Grid speed of light, gravitation.

Until the true value is confirmed, I am not sure which of the above is correct.

Chapter Eight

EDGAR CAYCE: THE HARMONICS OF THE SUBCONSCIOUS

In the early 1980s I read several books about Mr Edgar Cayce, a psychic, sometimes called The Sleeping Prophet. He was born on 18th March 1877 on a farm at Beverly, close to Hopkinsville, Kentucky, and during his lifetime became known and revered by thousands of people. He displayed abnormal powers from the tender age of six and claimed he could see visions of people and sometimes departed relatives.

One of his remarkable accomplishments was being able to sleep with his head on his schoolbooks in order to learn his lessons.

At the age of 21 he developed a paralysis of the throat muscles which caused the loss of his voice. Doctors could not find a physical cause, and in frustration he asked a friend to put him into a hypnotic sleep so that he could analyse his own problem during the trance state. He recommended certain medicative and manipulative therapies which cured his throat problem and restored his voice to normal.

It was not long before he discovered that he could solve people's medical and other problems when in the trance state. When he died on 3rd January 1945 at Virginia Beach, Virginia, he left behind over 14,000 documented records, called readings, that he had carried out for over 8,000 people. These records are now preserved at The Edgar Cayce Foundation, located at 67th and Atlantic Avenue, Virginia Beach, Virginia, United States of America.

It is not my intention to write a comprehensive story about the life and accomplishments of Edgar Cayce as there are many other books and writings which tell of this in great detail.

What interested me was the birthplace of Mr Cayce and the geographic positions where he was able to carry out his trance readings with the most success and ease of mind. He did much of his work in the area of his birthplace, but when he moved around the countryside he seemed to encounter nothing but strife and disillusionment. All the plans he and others had in order to bring his gifts to the public seemed to end in disaster.

At one time, tentative plans were made by one group to build a hospital in Chicago. Another group chose a site within 100 miles of Dayton. Readings by Edgar vetoed these and other suggestions, and gave explicit instructions to build at Virginia Beach. It would be best here for his health and psychic abilities. Over and over the inner voices said, Virginia Beach, Virginia Beach.

During my earlier research I had discovered that the human body is harmonically tuned within a certain range to all the surrounding natural frequencies of light and gravity, etc., and there were indications that psychic and telepathic abilities can be enhanced in the few people who are most closely tuned to the basic harmonic values. Position could also play a part in this. For instance, the Russians have discovered that the number of major acupuncture points on the human body is 695 (speed of light reciprocal, gravity), and it appears that they position their psychics geometrically when they carry out experiments.

It is clear that Mr Cayce's psychic abilities were finely honed to the natural forces, but was his inner self trying to advise him to move to a geographic position that would lock him into almost perfect reception?

With this in mind, I contacted The Edgar Cayce Foundation and asked if they could provide me with information regarding the latitude and longitude of his birthplace and the research centre and hospital at Virginia Beach. I had already checked a number of other positions around the world where psychic-type healings had been carried out, and rough calculations indicated that location was a significant factor.

I received a very courteous and helpful reply from the Foundation and, several months later, a second letter which gave the positions requested. It was evidently a difficult task to pinpoint Mr Cayce's birthplace, as Beverly does not exist anymore on modern maps. Many letters had to be exchanged with people in the area before its exact location could be ascertained.

The positions given were:

Latitude:	Beverly:	36° 51' 00" north
	Virginia Beach:	36° 51' 00" north

Longitude:	Beverly:	87° 29' 00" east
	Virginia Beach:	75° 59' 00" west

This information was received some time ago, and the earlier publication I had intended was delayed until the present time because of the actions of others which caused the removal of my books from the market. Fortunately I am now back in business and the computer programs are now available to enable accurate calculations.

The first most interesting fact which was evident in the positions given by the Foundation was that the latitude values of Mr Cayce's birthplace and the eventual position he moved to at Virginia Beach were the same. This was most unusual.

The latitude of 36° 51' 00", given to the nearest minute of arc, was fed into the computer, and a more accurate harmonic value of 36° 50' 59.514396" or 36.84986512° was indicated—an error of around 50 feet.

When harmonically processed, this value could be associated with Unified Equation 3 if the speed of light value entered into the equation were 143,909.0655 minutes of arc per grid second. This value for light-speed was found to be associated with electromagnetic transmission.

The geometric distance to the north pole	= 53.150134 degrees
The geometric distance to the equator	= <u>36.849865</u> degrees
Difference	= <u>16.300269</u>

Harmonically:

16.30026 ÷6÷6÷6÷6÷6÷6÷6÷6÷6	= 2.6957666[-7]
Harmonic 26957666	= $\sqrt{[(2c + \sqrt{1/2c})(2c)^2]}$
Where 'c'	= 143,909.0655 minutes of arc per grid second

The unified harmonic would apply to both Mr Cayce's birthplace and Virginia Beach. The longitude value for Beverly gave the pure light harmonic of 144000 with a plus or minus margin of about 400 feet. This was derived from the great-circle distance to zero longitude at the same latitude. It would be interesting to know just how close to Mr

Cayce's actual place of birth in the old community of Beverly the calculated position turned out to be.

The longitude position that would theoretically be the best place at Virginia Beach for harmonic reception was calculated to be:

Longitude 75° 59' 27.96" west, or 75.9911 degrees.

This gave a great-circle distance to zero longitude, at the same latitude, of:

	3541.4672 minutes of arc
	= 59.0244533 degrees
Processed harmonically	= 59.0244533
Reciprocal	= 0.01694213 harmonic
Squared	= 2.8703579^{-4} harmonic
Divided by 2	= 1.4351789^{-4} harmonic

This is the harmonic of 143517.89 minutes of arc per grid second.

This was a great result because when the actual speed of light, equivalent to the gravity reciprocal, for the latitude of 36.84986512 degrees was checked on the computer using the Cathie/Maupin program, the value indicated was 143517.89 minutes of arc per grid second—a very accurate harmonic match.

All the parameters within a very small radius of error appear to show that Mr Cayce was born on, and urged by strong psychic suggestions to go to, a well-defined harmonic geometric position which enhanced his strange abilities.

The geometric position of the birthplace of an individual does seem to have a definite effect on the possible psychic abilities of the person. Also, geometric positioning in other areas on the Earth's surface appears to enhance this ability during psychic experiences. It would be interesting to check the birthplaces and operating areas of other well-known psychics in order to ascertain whether this is common to all.

Chapter Nine

POSSIBLE POSITION FOR HARMONIC EXPERIMENT

Every now and then a geometric position becomes evident that could possibly be used for experimentation based on the theoretical harmonic unified tables demonstrated in this book.

The following position came to my attention several weeks ago. At this time it is a piece of barren land, but maybe in the future someone will realise its significance. The harmonics involved at the geometric point are quite interesting.

Position:
Latitude 36° 55' 46.399116" south / Longitude 174° 49' 33.66354" east
Latitude 36.92955531° south /   Longitude 174.8260176° east

Harmonics:
The actual speed of light or electromagnetic speed of propagation at this latitude is 143517.1373 minutes of arc per grid second, as ascertained from the unified tables. If we subtract this value from the maximum speed of light of 144000 minutes of arc per grid second, we have:

$$144000.0000$$
$$- \underline{143517.1373}$$

Difference	482.8627
The square root of harmonic 4828.627	= 69.48832276
The reciprocal	= 0.01439090655
The harmonic of	**143909.0655**

(See tables.)

Also, if we divide the latitude by the basic harmonic of 6:
36.92955531 ÷6÷6÷6÷6÷6÷6÷6÷6÷6÷6÷6÷6

	= 1.6965203^{-8}
Squared	= 2.8781812^{-16}
Divided by 2	= 1.4390906^{-16}
Harmonic of	**143909.0655**

Position Longitude 174.8260176°:

174.8260176 - 90	= 84.8260176
Multiplied by 2	= 169.6520352 harmonic
Squared	= 28781.81304 harmonic
Divided by 2	= 14390.90655 harmonic
Harmonic of	**143909.0655**

There would not be too many positions available with these particular harmonic associations.

Chapter Ten

MORE HARMONICS OF STONEHENGE

In my last book, *The Bridge to Infinity*, I asked the question, "Who built Stonehenge and why did they build it?" What is the true purpose of this geometric pattern of gigantic stones, said to be at least thirty-five centuries old, standing like ghostly sentinels on the Salisbury Plain in the southern part of England? As the centuries have gone by, many different investigators have tried their luck at deciphering the mystery of the complex, and to date I consider that none of them have come close to the truth. So far the reasons given for the construction are far too mundane to explain the immense effort and meticulous planning necessary to erect the stones with such precision.

In my second book, *Harmonic 695*, I suggested the probability that Stonehenge could have been designed as a gigantic crystal set—a massive geometric device constructed in ancient times to serve as a transmitter and receiver of signals from the heavens. This conclusion was reached because many of the known measurements were very close to those found in my own research. Also, a peculiar fogging effect was evident on many photographs taken of the stones, which indicated that some sort of radiation was emanating from them.

I spent many months carrying out a calculator analysis of the geometric pattern according to the harmonic mathematical values I had discovered up to that time. I believe that this demonstrated without much doubt that the stone complex was constructed to the unified harmonics associated with the equations discovered in my research.

Now, several years later, I have the recently completed unified tables to use in order to carry out a more comprehensive survey. This now allows a more accurate analysis of the Stonehenge geometric patterns which will correct the small errors in some of the calculations. The overall conclusions will not be altered significantly by this, but will strengthen the theoretical argument that extremely advanced knowledge was made use of in the construction.

I have already carried out some initial calculations on the computer using the special grid programs, and found very accurate associations with the unified tables which comply very closely with the published government survey carried out in normal English measurements. It is my intention to publish the latest results in a separate pamphlet on Stonehenge at a later date.

At this stage I will demonstrate how Stonehenge has been placed on a geometric position which gives a very accurate correlation with the unified tables. This information was not included in the previous analysis.

The most reliable information to date on the latitude and longitude position of Stonehenge is:

Latitude 51° 10' 40.54" north / Longitude 01° 49' 29.032" west.

The great-circle distance from longitude zero to longitude 01° 49' 29.032" west, at latitude 51° 10' 40.54" north was found to be 4118.041289 seconds of arc (plus or minus about seven inches).

If this value is processed harmonically, we have:

	4118.041289
Squared	= 16958264.05
Squared	= 2.8758271^{14}
Divided by 2	= $\mathbf{1.4379136^{14}}$

The final value is a harmonic of 143791.36 minutes of arc per grid second. This is the reciprocal of gravity in the unified tables—in other words, the speed of light which is the reciprocal of gravity.

This single coordinate indicates without doubt that the stone complex was constructed on a position which harmonises with the gravitational forces of the unified fields of the Earth. How could this possibly be so, unless the construction and positioning were carried out with the help of extremely advanced mathematical and technical knowledge at the time? We are just rediscovering this knowledge which was known to our ancestors.

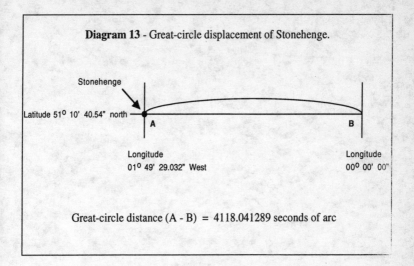

Diagram 13 - Great-circle displacement of Stonehenge.

Stonehenge

Latitude 51⁰ 10′ 40.54″ north

A

B

Longitude
01⁰ 49′ 29.032″ West

Longitude
00⁰ 00′ 00″

Great-circle distance (A - B) = 4118.041289 seconds of arc

Chapter Eleven

THE HARMONICS OF RENNES-LE-CHATEAU

In the early 1980s I read a book called *The Holy Blood and The Holy Grail* (written by a British author, Henry Lincoln, with co-authors Richard Leigh and Michael Baigent), and found it extremely interesting. It was suggested that Jesus survived the cross and married Mary Magdalene. They had children and eventually moved to France. The union was said to have formed the foundation of the Merovingian dynasty of Jewish kings. The weaving of historical events by the authors produced a convincing hypothesis but no definite evidence was shown to indicate that any particular area or ancient site had any direct connection with Jesus.

The main centre of interest appeared to be a small village, perched on the top of a hill in the south of France, called Rennes-le-Château:

Latitude 42° 55' 44.78" north / Longitude 02° 15' 49.306" east.

Once called Rhedae, a city of 30,000 people, it is now nothing more than a hamlet of roughly 200 residents.

The mystery began in 1885 when a young priest, Berenger Saunière, was sent to the Château to take up a position at the 800-year-old local church. The building had been badly neglected over the years and needed some costly restoration. The priest managed to obtain a small loan in 1891, and initial work began on improving the interior of the structure. As the work progressed, a hollow stone was discovered in the base of the altar and inside were found genealogical charts, documents and a number of Latin texts.

Saunière informed the Bishop of Carcassone of the discovery and was then sent to Paris where he was advised to contact a certain list of people who, it is said, had associations with a number of occult societies. The reason for the visit is not known but, on his return to the

Château, Saunière appeared to become extremely wealthy. He began to spend large amounts of money on the restoration of the church and generally live a life of opulence.

The book, *The Holy Blood and The Holy Grail*, goes into great detail regarding the history of the Château environs and points out that the Knights Templar had very strong associations with the area. The authors speculate that a vast treasure trove could be buried in the hills surrounding the Château, including the legendary treasure of Solomon's Temple in Jerusalem and possibly the Holy Grail itself.

It was obvious from their extensive research that Saunière had found something extremely important. He undoubtedly discovered some sort of treasure, but at the same time he also discovered a secret of immense importance. The Church showed great interest in the discovery. It is said that Saunière defied his Bishop with impunity on many occasions but was subsequently exonerated by the Vatican. The priest's secret appeared to be "more of a religious nature than political", according to Henry Lincoln.

All in all it was a great story, and I decided that at some future time I, myself, would carry out some research on the area when I had completed my own projects—then completely forgot about it.

That is, until a few years ago when out of the blue a book arrived in the post from a Mr David Wood of England. Called *Genisis*, the book was an extremely up-market production which covered, amongst other interesting information, a comprehensive ground survey of a large area surrounding Rennes-le-Château.

Mr Wood is a qualified surveyor and cartographer and owned a small reprographic company which placed him in the invaluable position of being able to reproduce accurate maps to scales suitable for investigation.

He reasoned that, "an intelligent early civilisation would leave signs, or markers, of a far more permanent nature than the written or spoken word... One thing which would meet these requirements would be sacred geometry."

"Much of the history of the Church of Rome is concerned with religious persecution... I was intrigued by what it could be which was so important that it warranted such intense suppression. I began to wonder whether the valley may contain something which in the opinion of Rome we were not meant to find. Could it be, as was also implied, that the valley held a much greater secret than treasure, buried or otherwise?... For centuries, Rome considered the pursuit of scientific knowledge to be evil, and I wondered if the valley held something of this nature. Alternately, could it be historical or religious knowledge potentially damaging to the infrastructure of the Roman Catholic Church?"

Thus David Wood set out on an intensive geometric analysis of the area surrounding Rennes-le-Château:

"The result of this work was initially the recognition and identification of an immense geometrical figure, indelibly marked on the ground, which I have called The Temple of Rennes. It is designed in a manner so perfect and so logical that it is undeniable; a deliberate and verifiable construction, so brilliant and on such vast scale that it staggers the imagination... It covers an area of 40 square miles and every part is marked by a mountain top, a church, an outstanding rock feature, or some intersection of carefully designed geometry. It is the largest such Temple ever discovered. It incorporates such detail as to obviate totally any possibility of the design being coincidence."

During the course of Mr Wood's investigation, he found that some of the geometric and mathematical values came very close to those that I had published in my earlier works. It was this that encouraged him to send a copy of his book to me for comment.

I was obviously very interested in the information, and on receiving the book I telephoned him in England in order to discuss his work and the possible link between his findings and my own. At the time I was not sure whether the connection was valid as his values were in English miles, and mine in nautical miles or minutes of arc measured on the Earth's surface. I suggested that he convert his measurements into geometric equivalents the same as mine, and recheck the data. I did not realise at the time that there was a definite mathematical link between British and geometric measure. The mile, foot, inch, etc., do not appear to be arbitrary lengths.

After this initial discussion with Mr Wood, I again put the problem aside as I did not have the facilities to carry out a full-scale investigation and my own work was taking up the majority of my time.

It was not until I had contact with Rod Maupin and we began to develop the computer program which enabled the calculation of great circles, etc., that I again became very interested in the Rennes-le-Château area. I now had a means to calculate very accurate distances between points on the Earth's surface (Rod's program calculates to an accuracy of fifteen decimal places), so I contacted Mr Wood once more and asked him if he could possibly supply me with survey maps of the

Château area and latitude and longitude positions of the sites of interest. He was extremely cooperative and, soon after, the required material arrived in the post: large-scale survey maps and a list of latitudes and longitudes (see below).

Coordinates of major positions in the Rennes-le-Château diagram:

Position	Latitude North	Longitude East of Greenwich
Centre of circle of churches	42° 54' 25.0"	2° 18' 43.2"
South seed	42° 54' 43.4"	2° 18' 39.3"
Rennes-les-Bains	42° 55' 10.3"	2° 19' 14.7"
North seed	42° 56' 50.1"	2° 18' 42.6"
North pentagonal apex	42° 58' 32.5"	2° 18' 46.0"
Rennes-le-Château:		
Tour Magdala	42° 55' 43.3"	2° 15' 46.4"
Church	42° 55' 44.8"	2° 15' 49.2"
Pech Cardou	42° 56' 14.2"	2° 19' 41.9"
Château d'Arques	42° 57' 15.0"	2° 22' 06.0"
Toustounes (head rock)	42° 56' 22.5"	2° 20' 56.4"
Bugarach	42° 52' 36.0"	2° 21' 09.5"
St Just	42° 52' 48.9"	2° 16' 04.7"

These were the main positions I fed onto the computer, but as the work progressed I plotted very accurate positions of a further 12 sites to extend the analysis. Before commencing the analysis I carried out a series of calculations in order to see if a correlation between British and geometric measure did, in fact, exist. Mr Wood had discovered that he could use measurements of one-mile units between points on the survey maps, and they appeared to fit perfectly with the geometric layout of the churches and other positions of interest.

It did not take me much time to discover that British and geometric measures are interlinked. The secret is hidden in the relationship between the radius and circumference of a circle. (See Diagram 14.)

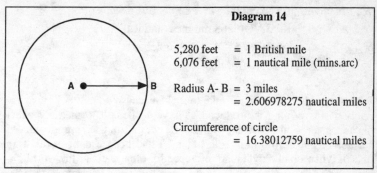

Diagram 14

5,280 feet = 1 British mile
6,076 feet = 1 nautical mile (mins.arc)

Radius A- B = 3 miles
          = 2.606978275 nautical miles

Circumference of circle
          = 16.38012759 nautical miles

If we now treat the circumference harmonically by the use of the six increment, then:

Circumference 16.38012759 x 6	= 98.28076554
98.28076554 x 6	= 589.6845932
Reciprocal	= 1.6958218^{-3}
Squared	= 2.8758116^{-6}
Divided by 2	= 1.4379058^{-6}
	= 143791.36 harmonic

The fractional error of the harmonic would be due to the conversion values. An exact conversion would be 2.9999918 miles—a conversion error of 0.5144832 of an inch. If we ignore the fractional error of conversion it can be seen without much doubt that British measure has a definite relationship with the geometric reciprocal of gravity acceleration. The geometric harmonic of gravity acceleration is 69545205 in the unified tables. (See Table 2.) The three-mile radius of the circle can be converted into a harmonic of 143791.36 minutes of arc per grid second—the speed of light for the gravity reciprocal. (Recent research indicates that the 'speed of light' is in fact an acceleration, but this is dealt with in other sections of the book.)

The next step was to study Mr Wood's initial plot of the area and see if I could get a correlation of his measurements on the computer. He stated in his book that the distance between the sister churches of Rennes-le-Château and Rennes-les-Bains was exactly three miles. I did not doubt that his measurements on the survey map indicated this.

I fed the latitude and longitude positions of the two churches supplied by Mr Wood into the computer and in a minute or so I had an answer. The distance given was slightly smaller than that given by Mr

Wood's analysis. The computer read-out gave a value of:

2.573040268 minutes (nautical miles)

or　　　　　2.960945579 British miles

This is an error of 206.20735 feet.

This would be an easy mistake to make because no matter how accurately a survey map is produced, it is very difficult to measure exact distances across it because of inherent errors in transferring the curved surface of the Earth onto a flat plane. I had been caught in this trap myself when I had only a map reference for other parts of the world.

However, I was in agreement with Mr Wood regarding the link because of my own mathematical findings. There was a correlation between British and geometric measure, but was it built into the geometry of the area?

I next tried the computer distance between Rennes-les-Bains and the library (Tour Magdala), built by Saunière a short distance from the church. This proved to be:

2.600966464 minutes of arc (nautical miles)

or　　　　　2.993081861 miles

This was closer, but again gave an error—36.52778 British feet.

If there was a direct correlation built into the pattern, then there must be another point just to the west of the library building. The clue to this further point was to be found in a later book by Henry Lincoln, called *The Holy Place*.

Mr Lincoln states in his book that Saunière built his Tour Magdala as far to the west as was possible within the confines of his hilltop village —perched, in fact, on and well nigh over the sheer drop of the escarpment. Saunière apparently had plans for another, much more grandiose tower. Just before his death in 1917, he signed a contract for the work.

The new library was to be about 60 metres high. Mr Lincoln calculates a position for the tower site using a six-mile distance from Arques Church and finds that it fell on the hillside below the Tour Magdala. Lincoln surmises, "Could this have been Saunière's intention to complete the alignment?"

Would this also allow for the missing 36-odd feet indicated on my computer? We may never know but it is certainly possible that the correlation of measurements could have been built into the geometric layout had Saunière completed his project.

Diagram 15

The first lines, plotted by Mr David Wood, which established the centres for the two circles.

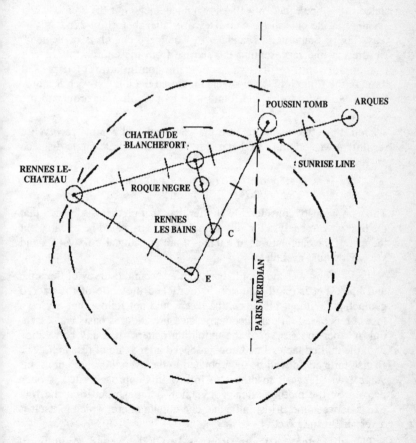

"C" and "E": Centres for the two circles

An interesting fact here was that the Tour Magdala was, according to the computer and site positions supplied by Mr Wood, 2.5455844 seconds of arc from the church—plus or minus about half a geodetic foot. (See the polar sections of the grid and the Earth's magnetic field for this harmonic value.)

The first major geometric line that Mr Wood had discovered lay between Rennes-le-Château and Arques, a few miles to the east. He stated in his book that "a well-known phenomenon of the area is when standing at the church the Sun rises over Blanchefort on 22nd July— feast day of Santamaria Magdala, to whom the church is dedicated." He drew a line representing the sunrise from the church to Château Blanchefort and, to his amazement, the continuation of it passed through the Church of Arques. He measured the line between Rennes-le-Château and Arques and found it to be six miles according to the scale he was using.

I fed these two positions into the computer and again I received a result that was contrary to that of Mr Wood. The great-circle distance proved to be:

	4.83681920169 minutes (nautical miles)
or	5.566006337 British miles

This is obviously considerably shorter than that plotted. I decided that the best way to analyse the full geometric pattern would be to carry out the rest of the calculations in minute-of-arc or nautical-mile values and see what would eventuate.

David Wood was the first to carry out an accurate survey of the area, and his expertise and intuition had cracked the code of the sacred geometry. Without his work, the rest would not follow, but my own research is based on pure geometric measure and this basis was essential in order to discover if the unfolding patterns had any correlation with the unified tables I had now produced after years of research. The British mile could well be incorporated in the overall design but at this stage I will leave it to others to follow this approach. It has been proved by the mathematical conversion demonstrated that the link exists between the British mile and one minute of arc, which in itself is a very interesting fact.

The distance between Rennes-le-Château and Arques of 4.83681920169 minutes was extremely close to 4.836535538—a difference of 1.7 geodetic feet. If we shift the decimal place harmonically and take the square root, we have 69545205 harmonic, which is the gravitational factor in the tables and the reciprocal of 143791.36 (har-

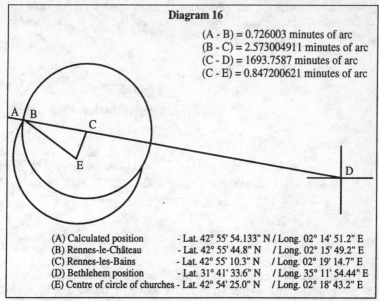

Diagram 16

(A - B) = 0.726003 minutes of arc
(B - C) = 2.573004911 minutes of arc
(C - D) = 1693.7587 minutes of arc
(C - E) = 0.847200621 minutes of arc

(A) Calculated position — Lat. 42° 55' 54.133" N / Long. 02° 14' 51.2" E
(B) Rennes-le-Château — Lat. 42° 55' 44.8" N / Long. 02° 15' 49.2" E
(C) Rennes-les-Bains — Lat. 42° 55' 10.3" N / Long. 02° 19' 14.7" E
(D) Bethlehem position — Lat. 31° 41' 33.6" N / Long. 35° 11' 54.44" E
(E) Centre of circle of churches — Lat. 42° 54' 25.0" N / Long. 02° 18' 43.2" E

monic of light). Things were starting to look very interesting.

Mr Wood had found that the pattern established two specific points from which two interlocking circles could be scribed. (See Diagram 15.)

The first circle to study was centred on the church at Rennes-les-Bains, the circumference of which passed through the church at Rennes-le-Château.

I had already established on the computer that the radius was:

2.5730402681 minutes of arc (nautical miles)

But a fractional correction of 2.545705 geodetic inches gave the following value:

2.573004911 minutes of arc (nautical miles)

The circumference of the circle was then found to be:

16.16666666 minutes of arc (nautical miles) relative

Which, when divided by 60, converts to:

0.2694444444 degrees (relative)

This was an amazing result because the 2694444444 harmonic is derived from Unified Equation 3 if the maximum speed of light,

144000 minutes of arc per grid second, is reduced by the harmonic of the constant mathematical value, phi, or ø, 1618.034—the Golden Section.

Maximum speed of light harmonic: 144000

- 161.8034

143838.1966 (reduced light speed)

Substituting in Unified Equation 3:

$$E = \sqrt{[(2c + \sqrt{1/2c})(2c)^2]}$$

$$= \sqrt{[(287676.3932 + \sqrt{1/287676.3932}) \times (287676.3932)^2]}$$

$$= \sqrt{[(2876763932 + 5895869800) \times (82757707)]} \text{ harmonics}$$

$$= \sqrt{(8772633732 \times 82757707)}$$

$$= \sqrt{72600305}$$

$$E = \mathbf{269444444} \text{ harmonic}$$

The second point established by Mr Wood was just to the south-west of Rennes-les-Bain, and using this as a centre he found that he could scribe a circle, the circumference of which passed through the church at Rennes-le-Château and also, much to his surprise, through several other churches at various points around the circumference. It was becoming very apparent that there was a definite geometric order in the layout of the religious centres, which at first sight appeared to be scattered randomly around the countryside.

The initial survey work by David Wood, and more recent investigations by Henry Lincoln described in his latest book, *The Holy Place*, have proved beyond doubt that a vast and complex geometric puzzle has been laid out in the area in order to conserve some sort of advanced knowledge.

My next step was to enter the latitude and longitude of the second point and Rennes-le-Château into the computer and find the distance between the two, which created the radius for the second circle.

The computed value:

2.50377007181 minutes of arc (nautical miles)

A very slight correction of 0.856146 geodetic feet or 10.27375 geodetic inches, and another set of quite startling harmonic values became evident:

Corrected radius	= 2.50362738 minutes
Divided by 36	= 0.069545205 (gravity harmonic)
Reciprocal	= 14.379136
Harmonic	= 143791.36 (gravity reciprocal, light)

Once again, the gravitational acceleration factor was evident in the pattern.

Attention was then given to the circumference of the circle which passed through all the church centres, which proved to be:

15.73075477 minutes of arc (relative)

At first there did not appear to be any harmonic significance to this value but then I decided to find the difference in the circumference of the two circles and obtained the following results:

Circle 1	= 16.16666666 minutes (nautical miles)
Circle 2	= 15.73075477 minutes (nautical miles)
Difference	= 00.43591189 minutes (nautical miles)
Divided by 6	= 00.072651981
Square root	= 0.26954

Another pleasant surprise. The 26954 harmonic is that which is derived from Unified Equation 3 if the speed-of-light factor for vacuum, 143891.36, is entered into the equation.

The next check was the distance between the two centres, (C) and (E). (See Diagram 15.) A quick computer calculation provided a value of:

0.84727040166 minutes of arc (nautical miles)

A fractional correction of 5.024 geodetic inches was all that was required to create further harmonics:

0.847200621 x 2 = 1.694401242 harmonic

The 1694401242 harmonic is one that links the magnetic fields with light and gravity.

This particular value can also be derived by the following formula:

$(\emptyset \times \pi)/3$ = 1694401242 harmonic, or
$(1618.034 \times 3.1415927) \div 3$ = 1694.401242 harmonic

The results so far were so accurate, with only fractional corrections necessary to be made to the computer calculations, that it came as no surprise that many of the other couplings of geometric points and distances resulted in harmonic geometric values associated with the unified tables and equations published in my earlier works. The patterns laid out on the ground appeared to be a practical demonstration, in mathematical terms, of the unified nature of the Universe.

The mathematical knowledge inherent in the network is so complex that it would take a full book to explain it all, so I decided to concentrate on the two circles constructed on Rennes-les-Bains and Rennes-le-Château and try to find what knowledge was hidden there which could possibly be related to Jesus—and, if so, why the Church was reluctant for the knowledge to be generally known. With this in mind, I tried various mathematical projections on the computer and studied the results.

I eventually discovered that if I projected a great-circle track from Rennes-le-Château that passed through Rennes-les-Bains, and extended it to the east, it ran right through the small township of Bethlehem—Jesus' birthplace. I was sure this must be the connection. There were secrets to be discovered in the relationship.

I now had a geometric puzzle before me: Rennes-le-Château, Rennes-les-Bains, two circles, and Bethlehem. It took me six weeks and a pile of computer paper to figure it out. The first point to tackle was Bethlehem itself. The computer had shown that the positions in the Château area all had harmonic links with each other, so in theory Bethlehem should be a harmonic point and the track angles and distances joining it with those in France should also be harmonic.

According to my *Times Atlas Index*, the latitude and longitude of Bethlehem are:

Latitude 31° 42' 00" north / Longitude 35° 12' 00" east.

I fed these positions into the computer as a starting point, and values very close to those previously discovered became apparent. Over the next couple of days, with the help of Rod Maupin's special program I fractionally altered the position until a clear set of harmonics became evident.

The computer indicated a point within the township 2,682 geodetic feet to the south-west of the *Times Index* position at:

Latitude 31° 41' 33.6" north / Longitude 35° 11' 54.44" east.

The unified computer tables will demonstrate that the actual 'speed of light' value changes according to latitude, although we always read a constant value due to relativity.

When I checked the calculated latitude at Bethlehem in the computer to ascertain the actual speed-of-light value at this level, I obtained the following, again astonishing result:

Speed of light, maximum, for gravity: 143,791.36 (±1).

The value for the latitude was right on the harmonic of the gravitational acceleration reciprocal shown in the unified tables. There must be more, I thought. Something completely unexpected was unfolding here. The hunch that something would be found in the Bethlehem area was strong but I did not believe the mathematical evidence would be so direct.

Next was the computer conversion of the normal Earth graticule latitude and longitude values into the equivalent positions of Grid A and Grid B latitude and longitudes. The results:

Grid A: Latitude 20.65509079° north / Longitude 132.0065841° east

Grid B: Latitude 22.54629627° north / Longitude 143.8609090° east.

Grid B held the secret. The longitude value of 143.860909 was instantly recognisable as a perfect harmonic of the speed of light in air at 143,860.909 minutes of arc per grid second, in the unified tables.

But what of the latitude of 22.546296277°? The answer lay in the difference of the displacements between the equator and the north pole of the grid:

90.00 - 22.546296277	= 67.45370373
67.45370373 - 22.546296277	= 44.90740746
44.90740746 x 6	= 269.44444 harmonic

Here again was a mathematical relationship with Unified Equation 3: the 26944444 harmonic.

I believe there is something extremely profound here, but I do not think it is my place to speculate. I will leave this to others and get on with the job of solving the geometric puzzle relating to this point and Rennes-le-Château.

The track and distance between Rennes-le-Château, Rennes-les-Bains and Bethlehem was the next step in the analysis, and this turned out to be a real headache. The computer indicated very close harmonic values:

Bethlehem - Rennes-les-Bains: 1693.7587 minutes of arc

Bethlehem - Rennes-le-Château: 1696.3316 minutes of arc

Very close, but not good enough. I was not satisfied with these results. They did not give me an accurate tie-up with other known values which should be present if the computer positions were correct. It took me several weeks to find an answer. I finally came to the conclusion that there was a bit missing. The value of 1696.3316 (Bethlehem to Rennes-le-Château) was not far off 1697.056274, which is the square root of the harmonic of twice the speed of light, maximum, 288000. If I extended the track to the west to allow for this, I wondered what the value of the missing portion would be.

A quick calculation and fractional correction gave an answer of:

$$0.726003 \text{ minutes of arc}$$

Square root of 7.26003 harmonic $= 26944444$ harmonic

Again we have an answer derived from the Unified Equation 3 when the maximum speed of light is reduced by the 1618.034, or ø harmonic.

The calculated point west of Rennes-le-Château proved to be:

$$\text{Latitude } 42° 55' 54.133'' \text{ north } / \text{ Longitude } 02° 14' 51.2'' \text{ east}$$

The track angle from the Château:

$$282.400207 \text{ degrees} = 16944.01241 \text{ mins of arc} = (\text{ø} \times \pi)/3$$

I also found that the calculated point was 3.299077382 from Rennes-les-Bains. Harmonically:

$3.299077382 \div 6 \div 6 \div 6 \div 6 \qquad\qquad = 2.5455844^{-3}$

(See grid harmonics, the Earth's magnetic field.)

The mathematical evidence gives a very strong indication to me that the position to the west is a valid point and that some evidence could be found there, either on the surface or underground, which could be of some significance. Could this be the position that has the direct geometric association with the birth of Jesus? Harmonics of light and gravity are the connecting links.

There is much further investigation yet to be done, and my mathematical probe into the mystery will be added to the growing pile of speculations published by other researchers. My computer has told me more things about this area than I have demonstrated, but I did not wish to confuse the issue with too much detail.

Other investigators can flesh out the bones of the geometric patterns presented here for independent analysis. If there are errors in my work, then they will be found and corrected.

Chapter Twelve

THE HARMONICS OF A METEOR CRATER

The most well-known so-called meteor crater in the world is the one in the State of Arizona, United States of America. Many attempts have been made to ascertain the age of the crater and the various publications that I have read give values of 2,000, 3,000, 22,000, 25,000 and 50,000 years old. It is obvious from this that everybody is guessing and that much more data will be necessary before the true age can be accurately assessed.

The diameter of the basin-shaped crater is given as 1,265 metres and the depth 175 metres, and it is situated between Winslow and Flagstaff townships on a large flat plateau. The walls of the crater rise from 37 metres to 50 metres above the surrounding plain.

In 1905, attempts were made to find fragments of any meteorite mass that may be buried deep below the centre of the crater, and bore-holes and shafts were sunk to a depth of 607 feet where undisturbed layers were found. No material was discovered. In 1920 another search was made in the area of the southern rim, again without success. There was a considerable amount of what was thought to be meteoric iron found on the surrounding plain and because of this the scientists have concluded that the crater was definitely formed by a meteor which was almost completely vaporised at the instant of impact. Regardless of this general view, many scientists believe it to be of volcanic origin.

Because of the perfect bowl-shape I found it hard to believe either of these explanations. It is thought that a meteor came in at a very low angle and blasted out this gigantic crater, but I cannot see how a perfectly round hole could be formed under these circumstances.

If it is volcanic in origin, where is the evidence of this in the underlying strata? Or why are there no traces of volcanic lava? Nothing but a few traces of iron scattered around the plain. I had a feeling that there must be some other explanation and wondered if a check of the geometric position would show evidence of other forces which could have caused the cataclysmic explosion.

My *Times Index* gave a position of:

Latitude 35° 01' 00" north / Longitude 111° 03' 00" west.

A quick calculation on the computer indicated that a very slight adjustment to the latitude and longitude values would give the following harmonic results:

Latitude 35° 00' 55.357" north / Longitude 111° 02' 58.7616" west

First, the latitude:

90° - 35.01537694°	= 54.98462304°
54.98462304 ÷ 6 ÷ 6 ÷ 6	= 0.25455844 harmonic

As will be seen in other sections of this book, the 25455844 harmonic is built into the polar segments of the grid system and is the reciprocal of harmonic 3928371, the difference between the two Earth magnetic fields.

Next, the longitude: 111° 02' 58.7616" west

111.04965601° - 90°	= 21.04965601
21.04965601 x 6 x 6 x 6 x 6 x 6 x 6 x 6	= 5892556.5
Reciprocal of 5892556.5	= 1.6970562^{-7}
This value squared	= 2.88^{-14}
Harmonic	= 2c maximum

The explosion, whatever the cause, appears to have occurred on a very precise position on the Earth's surface. I believe that this would rule out the theory that a meteorite was the cause.

The geometry of the position could indicate possible volcanic origin, but lack of other evidence of this type of geological disturbance would also make this theory fairly remote.

What then are we left with? Unnatural causes? Could it be that some time in the remote past, somebody or something carried out an experiment that got out of control?

Chapter Thirteen

THE HARMONICS OF THE MOON

Approximately 20 years ago I spent an evening going through some back copies of *Scientific American* magazine and came across a two-page spread of a photo of a large Moon crater. It is so long ago now that I forget the date of the magazine issue and the name of the crater, but the photograph was so clear it caught my attention and I decided to have a closer look at it. I placed the photo on the floor under a strong clear light and studied it for about half an hour through a powerful magnifying glass. Gradually I became aware of a number of unusual features that defied explanation. I became quite excited and called out to my wife to come and have a look.

I made no comment about what I had seen through the glass and left her to quietly study the crater for the next 20 minutes or so. Suddenly she too became quite excited and exclaimed, "There are buildings of some sort in there and, look, there appears to be a road going out over the lip of the crater!"

Her observation was almost identical to mine. I had spotted what appeared to be a cluster of buildings in the centre of the crater floor and lines running from them that could have been roads. One of them extended across the crater and up the sloping wall, then through what appeared to be a cutting, to emerge outside the crater into the surrounding terrain. If what we were seeing was not an illusion, the Moon was obviously occupied by intelligent beings who were actively engaged in some project. The question was, were they aliens, or our own people who had reached the Moon without our knowledge?

A few weeks later we had several people around to our home for discussions about the work I was doing, and the photo of the crater was amongst a lot of other material scattered around the living-room floor. Some of the guests had examined the photo and came to the same conclusions as my wife and I had. The next day when I was tidying up all my research material, I found that the magazine with the photo was missing. Almost certainly, one of the guests had walked off with it the night before. As I had not taken a record of the names and addresses of the visitors, I was unable to track it down and have not seen it since. From that time I have made a point of checking on strangers who wish to visit me and discuss my findings. If any readers are aware of this particular photo, I would much appreciate another copy.

Since then I have been extremely interested in all the information available relating to the Moon and constantly look for more evidence to confirm that it is inhabited.

I could never understand why NASA went to all the trouble and expense to send our astronauts to the Moon, then suddenly scrap the project and wind down the whole space program. Did they, too, discover that the Moon was already occupied and that the technology behind the rocket program was out of date? I believe that this could well have been so. The evidence I now have shows that the secrets of gravitational energy and travel in space-time have been available to a small group of our own Earth scientists for many years. Secret groups have had access to this knowledge from historical times, and our present-day technology is now enabling them to use it.

Apart from the information leaking out over the years regarding strange activity on the Moon's surface, the satellite itself raises many questions regarding the fact that it exists in its orbit around the Earth at all. None of the astronomy books I have read has satisfactorily answered the question of the Moon's existence.

The possibility that the Moon broke off from the Earth while it was still fluid, as a result of solar gravitational forces, has been discounted because of the analysis of lunar rocks brought back during the space program. The chemical differences between the Earth and the Moon are too great to support this.

The theory that the Moon wandered into the solar system from outer space and was captured by the gravitational field of the Earth has also been discounted because of the Moon's almost circular orbit. If the Moon had been captured in this manner then the orbit, in theory, would be elliptical. The possibilities of a near circular orbit are too remote even to be considered.

The possibility that a double planetary system was formed by accretion from the same ring of dust has also been considered but so far there is no evidence to back it up.

The Moon has many strange attributes which makes it unique in the solar system. It is roughly 400 times smaller than the Sun, but it is also 400 times closer. Because of this, the Moon covers the disc of the Sun perfectly during an eclipse.

According to the physics books, the acceleration of the Moon towards the Earth = 0.0089 feet per second squared

Divided by 6076 (6,076 feet equals one minute of arc on the Earth's surface) = 1.4647794^{-6} minutes of arc per second squared

Multiplied by 60 = 8.7886767^{-5} seconds of arc per second squared

Divided by 9 and multiplied by 8 twice, to convert to grid time

= 6.9441396^{-5} seconds of arc per grid second squared

From this it appears that the acceleration of the Moon towards the Earth has an affinity with the harmonic of the speed-of-light reciprocal, maximum, 6944444·.

This would be consistent with the geometric unified theory because the speed-of-light harmonic reciprocal is created by the gravity harmonic. The calculated value would vary fractionally if perfect conversion factors could be obtained. At this stage we can only rely on average values.

The gravitational association in the Earth-Moon relationship suggests that some of the other geometric values connecting the two bodies could have a harmonic basis. I spent the next few days searching through the astronomy books and found several geometric measurements which backed up the harmonic theory.

What I found was that the Moon does not actually revolve around the Earth as it would first appear. What in fact occurs is that the two bodies mutually revolve around their centre of mass. This point is called the barycentre. One complete revolution occurs during one sidereal month. Calculation by modern instruments shows that the mean distance of the barycentre from the centre of the Earth is 4,672 kilometres Therefore, the point of revolution is approximately 1,694.58 kilometres below the Earth's surface.

In order to check the possible harmonic relationship of these values, it is necessary to convert them into minute-of-arc measure related to the Earth's surface. The results are as follows:

4671.820512 km (round figure given 4672) = 2522.628529 minutes

Radius of the Earth in minute-of-arc values = 3437.74677 minutes

Therefore,

3437.74677 - 2522.628529   = 915.118241 minutes

Therefore, the barycentre is 915.118241 minutes or nautical miles below the surface of the Earth. So, the relative difference between the barycentre from the Earth's centre and the Earth's surface is equal to:

2522.628529 - 915.118241   = 1607.510287

Harmonic extension:

1607.510287 x 6 x 6 x 6   = 347222

347222 x 2   = **694444**

So here again we have the harmonic of the speed of light (maximum) associated with the Earth-Moon centre of mass.

The next thing I looked at was the geometrics of the Moon's orbit. Several different values were given in the astronomy books for the mean distance between the centre of the Earth and the centre of the Moon during its almost circular orbit. I chose to use the value given in the book, *The Exploration of the Universe*, by Abell, Morrison and Wolf (1987). In this book it is stated: "The best determination to date gives the distance from the centre of the Earth to the centre of the Moon the value 384,404 km, with an uncertainty of about 0.5 km."

But the most interesting fact given in this book is that the diameter of the Moon divides into the circumference of its mean orbit <u>695</u> times.

Diameter of the Moon:

$(2\pi \times 384404) \div 695$ = 3,475 kilometres

It then goes on to say that the most accurate calculation of the Moon's diameter to date is 3,475.9 kilometres, with an uncertainty of a few hundredths of a kilometre. In order to compute a very accurate value related to geometric harmonics, in previous work I found that it was necessary to fractionally alter the mean radius of the Moon's orbit and the given diameter.

I settled on a value of 3475.804269 kilometres for the diameter of the Moon, which was very close to the given margin of error, and a mean orbital radius of 384403.4591 kilometres, which was also very close to the given margin of error.

So, with a calculated mean orbit of 384403.4591 kilometres radius, the circumference would be: $= 2415278.167$ km

Divided by the Moon's diameter:

$2415278.167 \div 3475.804269$ $= 694.8832497$

Now the reciprocal of harmonic 694.8832497 is 0.001439090655, or the harmonic of 143909.0655 minutes of arc per grid second, which is the velocity of propagation of electromagnetic waves, demonstrated in other parts of this book.

When this value is entered into Unified Equation 2, the results give the harmonic difference between the Earth's magnetic fields "A" and "B", which is equal to 3928371.

The mean orbital radius of 384403.4591 kilometres creates another set of very interesting harmonics if the area enclosed within the circumference of the orbit is calculated. A radius of 384403.4591 kilometres is equal to 207565.1514 minutes of arc or nautical miles. The area of the enclosed plane with this radius is equal to 1.3535015^{11} square minutes (nautical miles).

If we convert the value harmonically by the multiplication of 36 for square measure:

$1.3535015 \times 36 \times 36 \times 36 \times 36 \times 36 \times 36$ $= 2.9462782^{20}$

Multiplied by 2

$2.9462782^{20} \times 2$ $= 5.8925564^{20}$

Reciprocal $= 1.6970562^{-21}$

Squared: $= \mathbf{288^{-42}}$

It appears that the orbit of the Moon has a direct mathematical relationship with the harmonic of twice the speed of light.

Other snippets of information about the Moon from the astronomy books are as follows:

The mean average distance from the surface of the Earth to the surface of the Moon is:

203374.4252 minutes of arc (or nautical miles), which is:

$= 3389.573753$ degrees (relative)

$3387.573753 \div 2$ $= 1694.786876$ harmonic

At particular points in its orbit, the distance would produce a harmonic of 169444.

The axis of rotation is not perpendicular to the plane of its orbit, but forms an angle   = 83.31666 degrees

This value squared   = 6941.666

This is close to the 69444 harmonic.

The average inclination of the Moon's orbit from the elliptic is:
                       = 5.1453 degrees

This varies by 0.3 degrees around its average value, with a period of 173 days.

90° - 5.1453°   = 84.8547 degrees

If we make a fractional correction to this, which is well within the variation:

84.8528136 x 2   = 169.7056272

Squared   = 288 harmonic

Also:

84.8528136 x 60   = 5091.168816 minutes of arc

Divided by 2   = 2545.5844

(See polar grid squares and the Earth's magnetic field.)

There are obviously many odd things about the Moon. Strange activity on the surface, strange transient lights moving about, dome-shaped structures that appear and disappear, conventional-type buildings, strange machines working in the craters. This and much more has been pointed out in various publications regarding the Moon. I will leave others to cover this type of research. My interest is in the geometric placement of our close neighbour.

What intrigues me is that the harmonic values discovered on my computer are related directly to the length of one minute of arc on the Earth's surface. Is this a natural mathematical relationship, or is this trying to tell us that the Moon is an artificial structure? Was it placed there for some purpose some time in the distant past?

Ask your friendly astronomer for some answers and watch him scratch his head.

Diagram 17 - The Harmonic Geometrics of the Moon

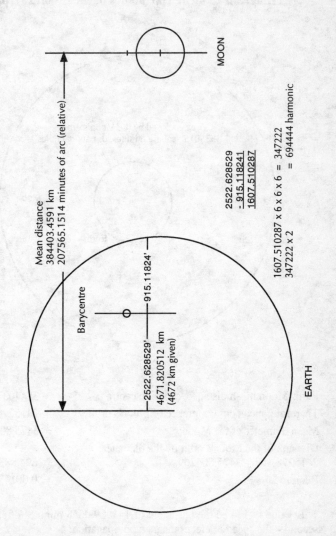

MOON

Mean distance
384403.4591 km
207565.1514 minutes of arc (relative)

```
  2522.628529
-  915.118241
  1607.510287
```

1607.510287 x 6 x 6 x 6 = 347222
347222 x 2   = 694444 harmonic

Barycentre

915.11824'

2522.628529'

4671.820512 km
(4672 km given)

EARTH

Diagram 18 - The Harmonics of the Moon's Orbit

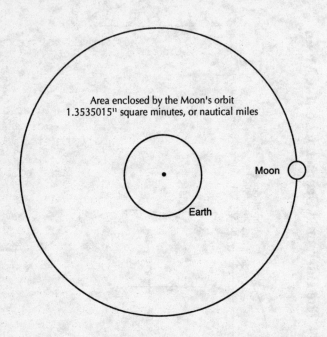

Area enclosed by the Moon's orbit
1.3535015" square minutes, or nautical miles

Moon

Earth

Earth-Moon mean distance, centre to centre	= 384403.4591 km
Therefore, mean circumference of Moon's orbit	= 2415278.167 km
Mean diameter of the Moon	= 3475.804269 km
Division of the Moon's orbit by the diameter: 2415278.167 ÷ 3475.804269	= 694.8832497
Reciprocal	= 0.001439090655

This value would be the harmonic of 143909.0655 minutes of arc per grid second—the speed of electromagnetic propagation.

Chapter Fourteen

THE PYRAMIDS OF MARS

Mars, called the "God of War" by the Greeks and Romans because of its reddish colour, occupies the next orbital path out from Earth. During its brightest period it outshines all other heavenly bodies except Venus. The distance from the Sun varies from 206,000,000 kilometres minimum to 249,000,000 km maximum, and at its closest proximity it comes to within 58,400,000 km of Earth. The oppositions occur at mean intervals of 780 days. The diameter of the planet is 6,794 km at the equator and 6,759 km at the poles, which makes it roughly half the size of Earth.

There has been much attention given to Mars over the last few years and NASA has carried out several photographic missions and landed hardware packages for scientific investigations of the planetary surface.

It is said that, apart from the Moon, this planet will be the first stepping-stone of man for the colonisation of the solar system and future ventures out into deep space. The surface conditions are desert-like, the atmosphere very tenuous and composed of ninety-five per cent carbon dioxide, roughly two per cent nitrogen, between one and two per cent argon, with the rest being made up of water vapour, carbon monoxide, oxygen, ozone, krypton and xenon. Strong winds sweep across the surface due to extreme temperature changes, making the general conditions inhospitable for human occupation. This will be overcome by the construction of sealed underground and surface stations similar to those being planned for the Moon.

There has been much speculation, since observation of the planet began, regarding the possibility that intelligent beings once lived on the Martian surface. Until the advent of the NASA probes, it was believed that the surface of Mars was criss-crossed with a complex system of canals to carry water from the snow-covered poles to the more arid areas. Close-up photographs soon destroyed this myth, but other evidence became visible which raised the question once again. Was Mars once the home of a thriving, intelligent race of beings that had access to advanced scientific knowledge?

Close observation of some of the thousands of photographs taken of the surface features indicates the distinct possibility that an intelligent race did in fact inhabit the planet. Unusual geometric patterns in several areas appear to be created by the remains of ancient cities, and a number of large formations of pyramidal shape seem to be too geometrically perfect to have been the work of nature.

Mathematicians have carried out extensive studies of the pyramid forms and have come to the firm conclusion that intelligent beings constructed them in the distant past.

Another startling find on several of the photographs (particularly *Viking* frames 35A72,73,74) which cover 350 square kilometres, taken of an area called Cydonia, is what is now known as "The Face on Mars". Computer enhancement has shown that the mysterious formation is a perfect, gigantic sculpture of a humanlike face. The position is given as latitude 41° north and longitude 9.4° west. The size, approximately 1.6 miles long, 1.2 miles wide, with the height at least 1,650 feet above the surrounding desert. The latitude position could indicate that the sculpture-like mound is not a natural formation.

Displacement from the pole	= 49 degrees
Displacement from the equator	= 41 degrees
Difference	= 08 degrees
	= 28800 seconds of arc

The harmonic of twice the speed of light (geometric).

Other publications have gone into great detail regarding this formation, so we will leave speculation on the purpose behind this possible evidence of occupation by our ancient neighbours in space and concentrate on one of the large pyramid-type structures a few miles to the south-west. This particular edifice has been named the D & M Pyramid.

I was not aware of the work carried out by other investigators regarding the geometric placement and possibly very accurate geometric construction of these formations until I was contacted by a scientist friend in England. He had noticed certain similarities to values I had discovered in my work dealing with the geometric unified nature of the Universe, and sent me copies of the data published by Richard C. Hoagland in America.

The Hoagland analysis of the Cydonia region demonstrated the geometric connections between many of the formations, and special attention was given to the D & M Pyramid. I am told that two years of work went into the mathematical probe of this one.

The photographs show a fairly clear outline of a five-sided pyramid which has allowed the investigators to make quite accurate calculations regarding the base angles and latitude position on the surface.

If the measurements presented by Mr Hoagland are accurate, then the base of the pyramid covers a huge area. By interpolation, the length of the structure appears to be:

4.411764705 minutes-of-arc long

and   3.970588235 minutes-of-arc wide

This would give a ratio of width to length of 1 to 1.1111111, which is quite remarkable. Nature could hardly come up with a coincidence such as this.

I was asked to check over the given values and see if I could verify them or find close approximations with my own work in geometric harmonics.

Inherent within the base angles were two harmonic values, 144 degrees and 69.4 degrees. The Hoagland analysis gave the value as 69.4 degrees, but I believe the actual value to be closer to 69.4444· (repeating decimal). This would be similar to my calculations for the geometric maximum for the speed of light, 144,000 minutes of arc per grid second, and the harmonic reciprocal.

The latitude position was given as 40.868 degrees north. Computer analysis indicated a more accurate position of 40.86786451 degrees north (a difference of approximately 49.5 feet). (See Diagrams 19 and 20.)

The displacement from true north of the whole pyramid complex was given as 10.5 degrees towards the east. According to an updated theoretical analysis, this could be closer to 10.472603 degrees. The displacement would then have a direct harmonic association with the gravitational values derived from Unified Equation 3, as follows:

$10.472603 \div 6 \div 6 \div 6 \div 6 \div 6$ $= 1.3467853^{-3}$

Multiplied by 2 $= 2.6935706^{-3}$

                                    $= \textbf{26935706}$ harmonic

See value for 'E'.

This displacement also leads to a possible solution of the Tetrahedron theory related to the pyramid, by Richard C. Hoagland. The results will be published in a later paper.

The true gravitational 'speed' of light for the pyramid latitude 40.86786451 degrees (40° 52' 04.3122"), was found by computer to be 143466.1084 (±0.1567) minutes of arc per grid second.

If we subtract 143466.1084 from the maximum speed of light, 144000, we get:

144000 - 143466.1084	= 533.8916
533.8916 ÷ 6 ÷ 6 ÷ 6 ÷ 6	= 0.411953395 harmonic
Squared	= 0.169705599 harmonic
Squared	= 0.0288 harmonic

The 288 harmonic is twice the maximum speed-of-light harmonic, 144000.

The latitude value 40.86786451 degrees, treated harmonically, gives:

40.86786451 x6x6x6x6x6x6x6x6	= 411853914.3 harmonic
Squared	= 1.6962364^{17} harmonic
Squared	= 2.8772181^{34} harmonic
Divided by 2	= 1.43860909^{34} harmonic

This is the harmonic of the speed of light in air from the unified tables, 143860.909 minutes of arc per grid second (at the equator).

The actual speed-of-light and electromagnetic-propagation values relative to the pyramid latitude, calculated by computer within an extremely small margin of error using the world energy grid program, are:

Gravity	Air	Vacuum	Electromagnetic	Maximum
143466.1084	143535.6	143565.9	143583.33	143675

Apart from the gravitational value, the relative value for electromagnetic propagation is of particular interest. With a calculated error factor of plus or minus 0.31 minutes of arc per grid second, we can derive the following harmonics:

Maximum speed of light
(electromagnetic)   = 144000 minutes of arc per grid second
Relative speed of light
(electromagnetic)   = <u>143583.333</u> minutes of arc per grid sec
Difference   =   <u>416.666</u> minutes of arc per grid sec
416.666 ÷ 6   = 69.44444

Harmonic 6944444˙, the maximum speed-of-light harmonic reciprocal.

The 694444˙ harmonic can also be derived from the angle formed by the chords projected from the pyramid's latitude position to the equator and the north pole.

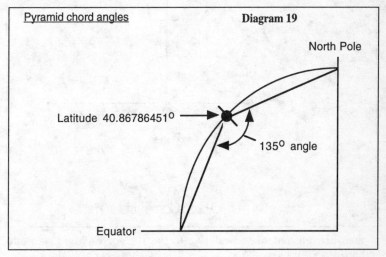

Pyramid chord angles   **Diagram 19**

North Pole

Latitude 40.86786451°

135° angle

Equator

$135 \div 6 \div 6 \div 6 \div 6 \div 6 \div 6$ = 4.8225308^{-4} harmonic
Harmonic shift (multiplication by 10)   = 4.8225308^{-3} harmonic
The square root of 4.8225308^{-3} = **0.06944444˙ harmonic**

If the D & M Pyramid is exactly what it appears to be, then we can assume that it has inner chambers similar to those in the Great Pyramid in Egypt and others scattered around the Earth's surface. The chord distances to theoretical positions within the pyramid, where chambers could have been geometrically placed, give values which can be related to the geometric unified equations. This aspect will be investigated further when more specific information is available.

The odds against the results of the mathematical evidence being so close to the unified harmonic values, if nature alone were responsible for shaping this structure, are so remote that we must consider the possibility or almost certainty that an ancient race once inhabited our close planetary neighbour. Could some of us be their descendants? Lots of questions, no answers—as yet.

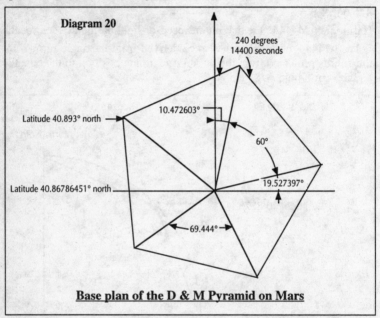

Diagram 20

240 degrees
14400 seconds

10.472603°

60°

Latitude 40.893° north

Latitude 40.86786451° north

19.527397°

69.444°

Base plan of the D & M Pyramid on Mars

Speed of light calculated relative to the surface of Mars (latitude 40.86786451°):

Gravity	Air	Vacuum	Electromagnetic	Maximum
143466.1084	143535.6	143565.9	143583.333	143675

The values are in minutes of arc per grid second relative to the surface of Mars.

Associated harmonic values related to the Matter-Antimatter Tables are as follows:

16939	16943	16945	16946	16951

Note: The harmonic geometric values are relative to any spherical body in space, and the length of one minute of arc on the surface would be calculated accordingly.

Chapter Fifteen

NIKOLA TESLA AND THE ELECTRIC CAR

In my earlier publications I demonstrated that Dr Nikola Tesla was fully conversant with the geometric unified nature of the Universe and made use of this knowledge to construct electronic apparatus in order to tap into the universal energy fields which permeate all of space.

His knowledge was so far ahead of his time that many of his inventions were not looked upon with favour and were quietly suppressed because they would have been a threat to many other contemporary ventures.

Information that has recently been made known concerns an electrically propelled car which he constructed in 1931. It is said that he removed the conventional engine from a Pierce Arrow car and substituted an electric motor of his own design. This was powered by what he called an energy receiver or gravitational energy converter, placed in front of the dashboard of the vehicle. The box containing the electronic apparatus was said to be 60 by 25 by 15 centimetres in dimension. There were 12 of the old-fashioned-type vacuum tubes in the box. Three of these were the 70-L-7 type. Connected to this was an antenna around 5.9 feet long. To make the converter work, two thick rods approximately 4 inches long, which protruded from the box, had to be pushed in. The car could reach a speed of 90 miles per hour with the motor at a maximum of 1,800 revs per minute.

Considering the modern-day problem of pollution, it is obvious that now is the time to re-invent the electric car. Some of the larger car companies are already designing vehicles which will be placed on the market in the near future. The efficiency of these cars, however, will not be anywhere near that of Tesla's because they will be powered by batteries which will require frequent recharging. Obviously the powers that be do not wish the general public to become aware that electrical energy, from a gravitational source, is available directly from the atmosphere.

Now that I have established a set of tables linking gravitational, light and electromagnetic harmonics, it is possible to search for evidence which will back up Tesla's claim that he was tapping into gravitational energy. The harmonic link to look for would be the 143791.364 value which creates the reciprocal of gravity acceleration in our reality or space-time continuum.

The length of the aerial in the car should show a harmonic relationship as it would have been necessary to design it in such a way that it was in harmony with the reciprocal gravitational factors. The given aerial length was approximately 5.9 feet. I found by calculation that a length of 5.914441183 feet gave the required relationship with the reciprocal gravitational harmonic, as follows:

5.914441183 feet	= 5.840461997 geo. feet
Divided by $6 \div 6 \div 6 \div 6 \div 6 \div 6 \div 6$	= 2.0863561^{-5} harmonic
Divided by 3	= 6.9545205^{-6}
Reciprocal	= 143791.364

The speed of light gravitational reciprocal. (See tables.)

It will be seen from the tables that the difference between the speed of light, 143791.364 minutes of arc per grid second (gravity reciprocal), and the maximum speed of light, 144000 minutes of arc per grid second, is 208.63561. This is the harmonic link with the aerial value of 2.0863561. The tapped energy is at a very high frequency and requires conversion to a much lower level for practical use.

I am sure that modern-day electronics specialists will have little trouble in reconstructing apparatus that will make available, once again, the unlimited energy which is inherent in our environment, now that the mathematical basis is known. I have tried to set up a team to carry out such a project in recent times but, once it becomes known, outside forces appear to intervene and cut off our funding.

Hopefully someone reading this will be more successful.

Chapter Sixteen

THE ROBERT ADAMS PULSED ELECTRIC MOTOR GENERATOR

Many inventors have striven to produce the ultimate free-energy machine that would help to break the monopoly control of power production held by the large international companies of today. The most well-known of these are Dr Nikola Tesla and Dr T. Henry Moray, both of whom managed to construct electrical apparatus that tapped energy directly from the gravitational field. In the case of Tesla particularly, the energy was then used to power conventional electric motors, which were not of great efficiency as shown in the previous chapter. I have no doubt that with the help of the harmonic unified theories demonstrated in this book, the secrets will be rediscovered in the not-too-distant future, but, in the meantime, other inventions are being made known to the public which could provide the breakthrough necessary to provide cheap and efficient power production.

A New Zealander, Mr Robert George Adams, born 2nd September 1920, is well on the way to doing this by publicly demonstrating new concepts in motor generating technology. At the early age of nine years, "Bob" commenced his venture into the mysteries of electromagnetics, radio-wave propagation and universal energy production. One of his first projects was to build himself a crystal set in order to tap into the universal energy field and listen in to these modified waves being broadcast from the early radio stations. The fact that these primitive assemblies of wires, coils and crystals hooked to makeshift aerial systems worked at all, mystified him. Where was the energy coming from? Scientists to this day, when asked this question, say the energy comes from the broadcasting station, but Bob was never satisfied with this answer. If thousands or, theoretically, an infinite number of crystal sets and radios were tapping energy from the broadcasting station, why is this supposed energy loss not detectable at the station? This was the time the young Adams was about to start on a lifetime venture into the exciting realms of electrical and electronic discovery and production of new and innovative circuitry.

At the age of 13 years, in 1933 he invented the solid-state amplifier consisting of two quartz crystals connected with cat's whiskers powered from 2 x 1.5-volt and 4 x 1.5-volt cells respectively and connected to the output of a crystal set, subsequently driving a loudspeaker (the forerunner of today's transistor and silicon chip).

He was too young to realise the importance of this accomplishment and its possible potential, except for one important point. If a crystal set, which is so small and of little weight, could receive and reproduce signals, why should a radio receiver be of such enormous dimensions and weight in those early wireless days of the 1930s? He figured that there must be a way to reduce such clumsy equipment, and had found the solution. Had he been older and wiser, naturally he would have persevered with the discovery. If he had done so, then electronics would probably be far more advanced than it is today.

In 1963 he invented the loudspeaker intercommunication telephone system and within three months secured a contract from Air New Zealand for a complete intercommunications system to cover the entire airport facilities.

Also in 1963 he invented the 'plug-in' printed circuit solid-state module/board now in common use in all modern electronic equipment. Industrial electronics control equipment, computers, telephone exchanges and communications equipment are but a few of the hundreds of applications for this device.

Then came the hybrid push-button telephone dialling system using electronics, but Strowger switching for line selection. He planned to incorporate this into the communications system being built for Air New Zealand but unfortunately the components required were not available in New Zealand during that time in the mid-'60s. This, too, would have been another early advance in the communications field and if pursued at the time would have heralded both types of telephones now in use, many years before they did in fact appear on the scene.

He built many very efficient battery-operated radios and power amplifiers and continually searched for new knowledge in the few publications available at that time. At the age of 14, in 1934, he left school and was offered an apprenticeship with a local wireless company in the town of Hastings.

He was 19 when he completed his time there, and he then left his home town to advance his knowledge and status in a position with an Auckland electronics company in their assembly plant. It was not long before he became, at the age of 22, the supervisor of factory production. At 27, he was the company's design engineer.

In the following years he spent time working on the control systems of broadcasting stations and designed much of the electronic equipment he was involved with. During this time he became a co-founder of Radio 1 New Zealand Limited.

Following this, he designed and commissioned sound and television studio recording systems and became New Zealand's first consulting engineer in broadcasting. In 1968 he published a manual which covered this type of engineering.

He also worked in some of the country's hydro-power stations as well as in the design and manufacture of highly efficient communications equipment for the country's major airline, Air New Zealand.

Among his many achievements are the following:

1970: Invented the Adams Pulsed Electric Motor Generator.

1970: Discovered the method of harnessing the collapsing field in an electric motor.

1975: Discovered a superior method of charging batteries (i.e., pulse charging).

1993: Discovered the procedure to engineer magnetic polarity reversal.

1993: Discovered an increase in the radiation pattern from the negative-energy, negative-time region of magnetic polarity reversal and the consequent radiation pattern measurement.

Other recent discoveries have been made which are yet to be made public.

It was during the late 1970s when Bob was in the formative stages in the development of the Adams Pulsed Electric Motor Generator that a small group of technical and engineering people started to take an interest in this particular area of his inventive abilities. Some of these people were personnel of Air New Zealand. At the time I was a Flight Captain and had interests along a similar line to Bob, and because of our sometimes offbeat approach to technical problems it was almost inevitable that some day we would meet. Sure enough, probably encouraged by our mutual connections in the airline, he phoned me one day in 1981 to discuss my publication which set forth my technical theories regarding the UFO enigma. Unknown to me, he had been following my work for a number of years and wished to delve deeper into the mathematical aspects of my research.

We had intermittent contact over the next few years and cautiously sounded out each other's ideas. Bob's machine slowly became a topic of discussion. He was pretty cagey at this stage and later became deeply involved with his invention and his own retail business, and our contacts became few and far between.

During this time he was being constantly plagued and frustrated by the negative attitude originating from the scientific establishment of the day. They refused to believe certain mathematical criteria pertaining to his machine's obviously outstanding performance. For 'belief' I probably should say 'acknowledge'. I was not aware of this, but when I eventually heard of his difficulties I was not surprised as I had suffered the same insulting behaviour for years. Thou shalt not rock the boat!

Bob contacted me again in 1985 and we became re-acquainted, this time on a more permanent basis, and since 1987 we have been constantly involved in each other's ventures and prime objectives.

Bob's machines have demonstrated the ability to generate free energy, unlike most of the theoretical models that are promoted as over-unity devices.

A general description of one of Bob's earlier machines, in broad terms, would be an electric motor and/or generator comprising a rotor consisting of a number of radially-arrayed permanently-magnetised poles, and a stator consisting of a number of radially-arranged permanently-magnetised poles, together with a number of wound poles.

The rotors' permanently-magnetised poles use ferrite magnetic cores and may comprise any even number of poles. The stators' wound poles employ steel or iron cores. The device is essentially a DC machine, but may be fed AC input with the use of a solid-state converter.

The rotor is unique in that it uses a number of similar-polarity permanent magnetic poles that are all south-going or all north-going.

A further set of wound poles may be radially arrayed in the stator and arranged in such a manner as to be fed energy that is excited by the back EMF energy from the poles of the rotor. Associated circuitry is provided to feed the energy back to the drive poles of the motor and/or battery.

This effect also overcomes the electrodynamic torque problems associated with conventional motor designs. As input power varies with the duty cycle pulse, the lower the input current, the higher the efficiency, the greater the power. At clip-off, the back EMF ceases; the collapsing field takes over, opposing the outgoing rotor magnet once again, thus increasing momentum.

A few other facts which relate to Bob's machines should be taken into consideration. If a machine is to run at unity, or better, it must first overcome those problems found in conventional machines. These, of course, are principally those of magnetic drag, hysteresis loss and eddy currents, all of which waste energy in heat and therefore require a cooling fan which in turn creates a further loss. His machines run cool in comparison with the conventional machines and therefore do not require cooling fans. In the conventional AC or DC machine, the internal heat of windings and stators reach boiling point within fifteen minutes. The Adams machine does not have this problem and runs almost at room temperature.

Another interesting feature is that if a small test model is to be constructed, it matters not whether standard, off-the-shelf alnico magnets or powerful magnets are used to prove that a machine can be built with over-unity capability. This has been demonstrated repeatedly with Bob's machines, using small and weak magnets. The only difference between using ordinary magnets like alnico and, for instance, samarium cobalt, is that you get greater energy output from the stronger magnets by way of their ability to detect and amplify the energy on a greater scale. Therefore, by use of the Adams pulsing system you can have a device using any ordinary magnets capable of not only 100 per cent efficiency, but also of being tuned into operating as a gate in detecting and delivering gravitational energy.

It has been found by experiment that by the application of the Adams Resonant Pulsed Frequency Equation and the Adams Pulsed EMG System, in combination with the Cathie Harmonic, Unified, Geometric, Light and Gravity Values, incredible energies can be very cleanly and easily made available.

Some recent comments published by Bob which relate to this are as follows:

"During the later months of 1992 I derived what I considered to be an equation for possibly the ultimate in rotary motor generator design. The purpose of this exercise was to ascertain whether further unconventional design features of the machine parameters, using this equation, proved certain theories which I had previously discussed with Mr Bruce Cathie, an internationally recognised New Zealand researcher in this field."

The work that we are both involved in now is to ascertain to what degree we can combine the harmonic unified theories discovered in my research with the construction of the advanced Adams pulsed machines.

We both believe that the ultimate in motor generator design could emerge from this collaboration. Efficiencies have already been increased, but the work is ongoing and there always seem to be more surprises round the corner.

The next step is to recreate the solid-state circuits invented by Tesla and Moray and again tap pure electrical energy from the all-pervasive gravitational fields. The unified gravitational and light geometric tables already give an indication of how this may be done with specifically tuned electronic circuitry. We may not make it, but it will be fun to try.

The information in this chapter is only a general overview of Bob's research into pulsed motor generator design and is not meant as a comprehensive explanation which would be necessary for the construction of a test model.

Diagram 21 - Adams Motor — General Construction

SW

12 — 36V

WATT METER

40°C
THERMOCOUPLE
TEMPERATURE
INDICATOR

OSCILLOSCOPE

THERMOCOUPLE PROBE

DRIVE WINDING TERMINALS

SPRING SET CONTACT NORMALS

STAR WHEEL COMMUTATOR

DRIVE WINDING

ROTOR

N

N

N

DRIVE WINDING

PERMANENT MAGNETS

PULLEY WHEEL

"S"

LOADMETER

"W"

NOTES

1. ADJUST SPRING SET CONTACT ASSEMBLY &
   STAR WHEEL COMMUTATOR FOR OPTIMUM PERFORMANCE.

2. REFER TD-102B FOR GENERATOR STATOR
   WINDINGS CONFIGURATION.

DATE	18th OCTOBER 1992
SCALE	APPROX ½
TOLERANCE	
QUANTITY	

ADAMS PERMANENT MAGNET ELECTRIC D.C. MOTOR GENERATOR
GENERAL CONSTRUCTION & TEST SET UP (MOTOR)

MATERIAL	
DESIGNED BY	ROBERT G. ADAMS
DRAWN BY	JOHN D. A. MARTIN

TD-102

COPYRIGHT © 1992
ROBERT ADAMS
WHAKATANE, N.Z.

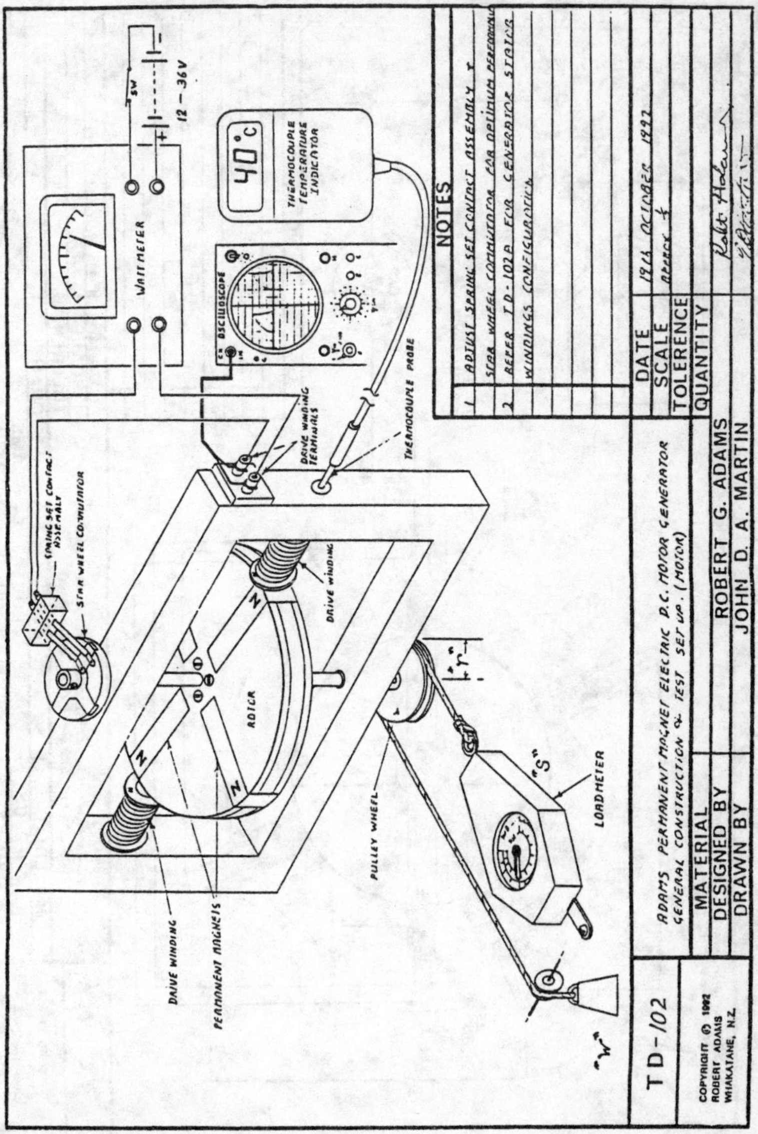

Diagram 22 - Adams Motor Generator — General Test Setup

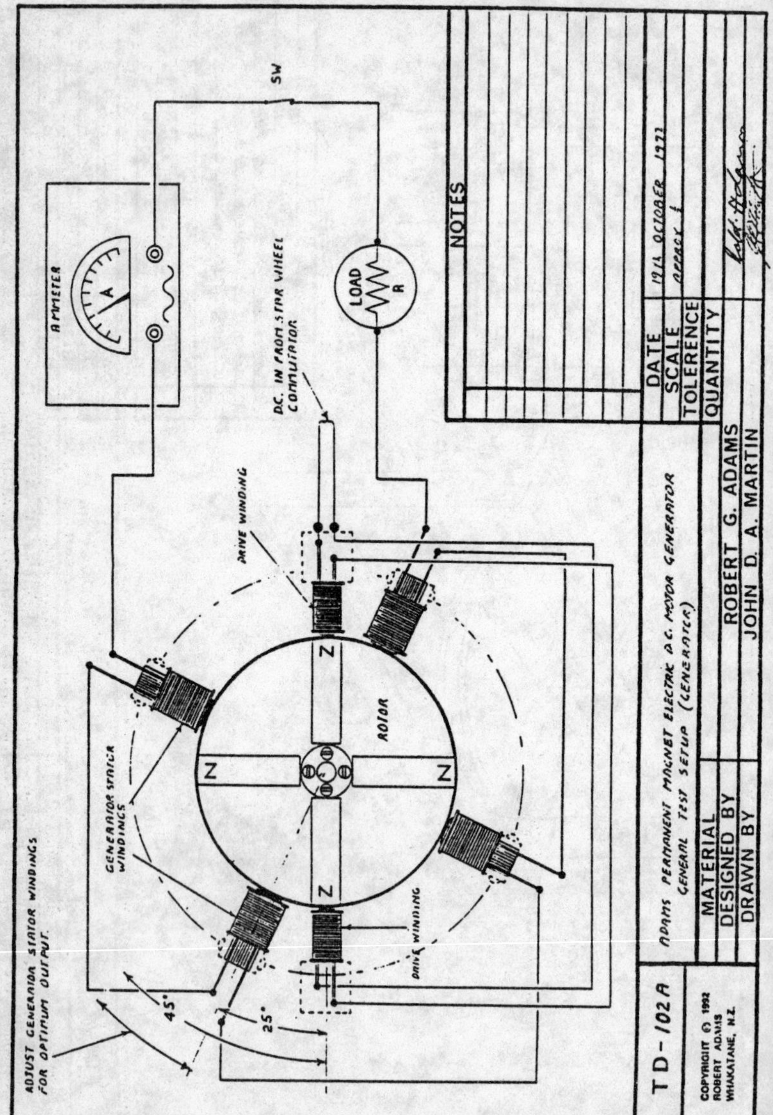

Diagram 23 - Adams Motor Four-Pole Rotor Assembly

NOTES

1. ALL SCREWS TO BE LOCTITED IN.

DATE	15th OCTOBER 1992	
SCALE	APPROX.	
TOLERENCE		
QUANTITY		

MATERIAL
DESIGNED BY   ROBERT G. ADAMS
DRAWN BY   JOHN D. A. MARTIN

FOUR POLE ROTOR ASSEMBLY.

TD-105

COPYRIGHT © 1992
ROBERT ADAMS
WHAKATANE, N.Z.

RESIN BONDING

PERMANENT MAGNET

HIGH DENSITY POLYURETHRNE FORM FILLER

SPLIT FLANGE
DRIVE SHAFT (BRASS)

PHENLIM DISC

UPPER SHAFT FOR UPPER BEARING
& 5STAR WHEEL COMMUTATOR ASSY.

LOWER SHAFT
FOR LOWER BEARING
& PULLEY WHEEL (BRASS)

PERMANENT MAGNETS

N N
N N

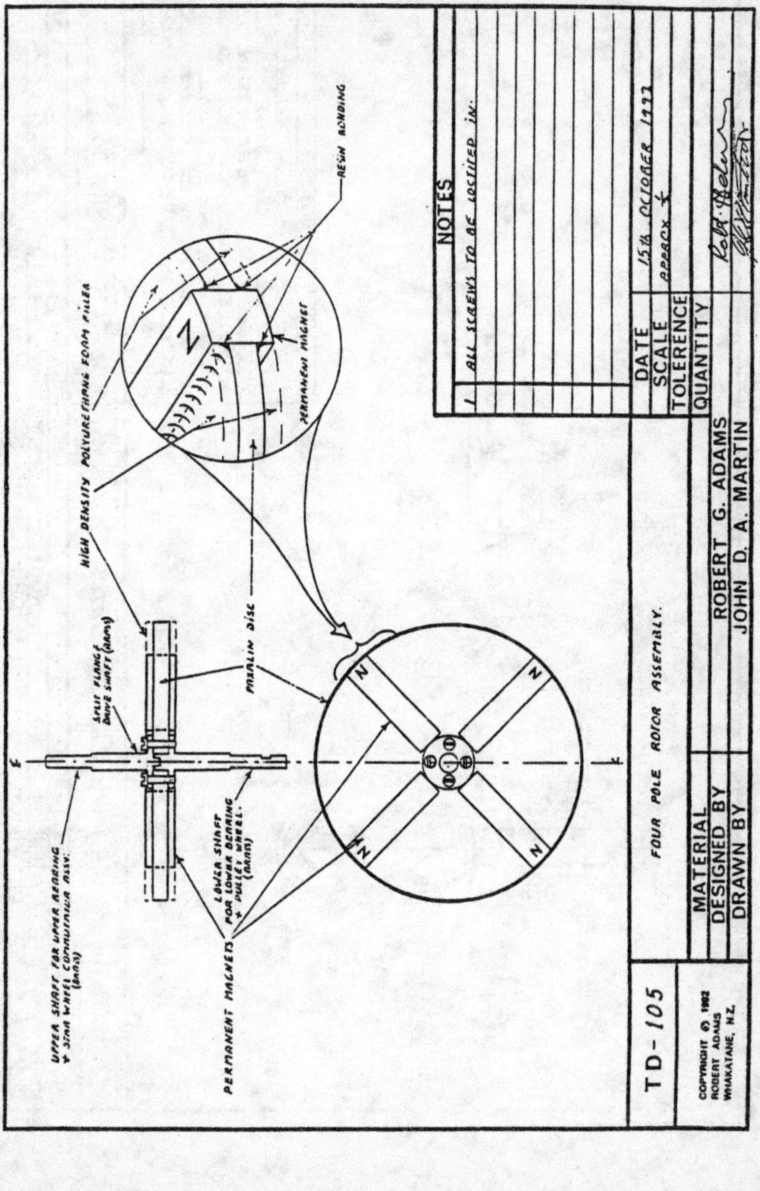

Diagram 24 - Adams Motor Star Wheel Commutator Assembly

NOTES

1 SURFACE "A" IS TO BE SKIMMED TRUE IN A LATHE & RE-BEDDED.

2 BRASS BUSH IS TO BE A PUSH FIT INTO PAXALIN DISC USING A SUITABLE LOCKING COMPOUND & A SNUG FIT OVER THE MOTOR ROTOR SHAFT END.

3 PAXALIN DISK IS APPROX 50mm IN DIAMETER.

DATE 14th OCTOBER 1992
SCALE NOT TO SCALE.
TOLERENCE
QUANTITY 1

STAR WHEEL COMMUTATOR ASSEMBLY.

MATERIAL
DESIGNED BY ROBERT G. ADAMS
DRAWN BY JOHN D. A. MARTIN

TD-104

COPYRIGHT © 1992
ROBERT ADAMS
WHAKATANE, N.Z.

BRASS BUSH
GRUB SCREW
LOCKWASHER
PAXALIN DISC
ROTOR SHAFT (BRASS)
RESIN BOND
BEVEL
COPPER COMMUTATOR (STAR)
NUT

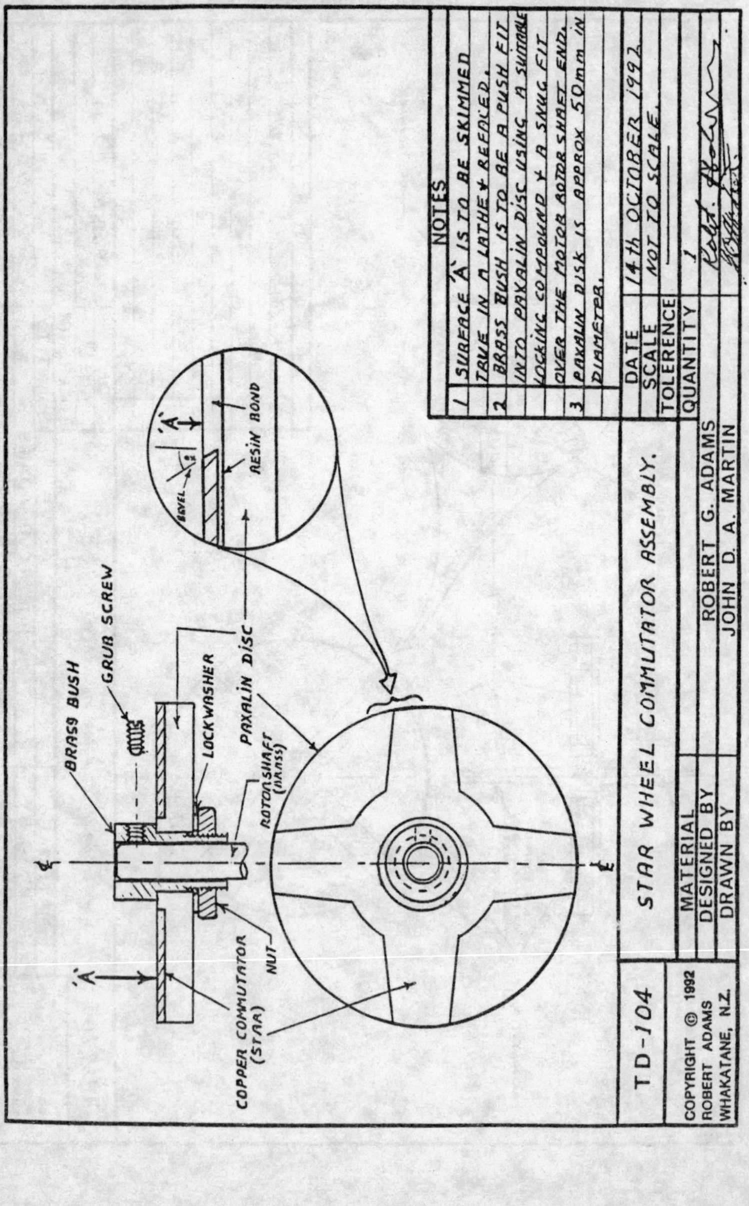

Chapter Seventeen

THE HARMONICS OF RIPPERSTONE FARM

I quite frequently call into a local second-hand bookshop, owned by a friend of mine, to browse through the stock for some light reading to fill in my spare time. As well as recreational material, I am also continually on the search for interesting bits of information to add to my research data, and quite often something turns up that merits particular attention.

On one recent visit I found my friend quietly reading a small, slightly dog-eared paperback at his desk during a quiet interval between customers. He has a general idea of the type of material I look for and said that maybe I should take the 14-year-old book with me and see what I thought of the strange story concerning the series of highly unusual happenings witnessed by a family on a farm in Wales, UK. He described some of the events and they certainly were bizarre. So I added the book to the others I had selected and returned home.

The next day I read the small book from cover to cover and had quite a strong feeling that the story was not a hoax. I therefore decided to carry out my own investigation to see if I could find some mathematical evidence to help verify the family's experiences.

The book was written by a journalist, Clive Harold, and was called *The Uninvited*, a "Star" book, published in 1979 by the paperback division of W. H. Allen & Co. Ltd, a Howard and Wyndham Company (44 Hill Street, London WIX 8LB, England, United Kingdom).

The events centred around Ripperstone Farm, situated on a clifftop overlooking St Bride's Bay, Wales. The tenant farmer, Mr William Coombs, his wife Pauline and their four children were subjected to a series of terrifying experiences over a period of many months, and to this day no logical explanation has been offered by those who have investigated the happenings.

It all started on 14th January 1977 when Pauline sighted a brilliant white light from the farmhouse window. It was fairly high in the sky and appeared to be hovering over a field at the bottom of the farm, near the cliff edge.

While she watched, the giant white ball carried out a slow, swaying pendulum-like motion before it dropped down swiftly towards the cliff edge and disappeared.

When Pauline's husband Billy came in for dinner after working around the farm all day, she told him of the strange and exciting incident. Next day he went down to the coast path along the clifftops to see if there were any markings of any sort on the ground where the light had descended, and was surprised to find a number of soldiers in camouflaged uniforms, several unmarked Army trucks, and about fifty frogmen milling around. He was told to keep away from the area. The Army and Navy were supposedly rebuilding the coast road because there had been a landslide, but their excuse for their presence seemed a bit thin.

From that time on, the family was subjected to a whole string of frightening and mystifying incidents. The television set and house wiring burnt out time after time, and the electrical power consumption of the farmhouse and electrical machinery increased out of all proportion for no apparent reason. Low-pitched humming noises were often heard around the property.

Glowing lights were seen outside the windows at night, and large space-suited figures were seen wandering around the farm. At one time, two odd-looking humanlike entities arrived at the house driving an odd-looking, silver carlike vehicle. One of them stayed in the 'car' while the other walked around the house and knocked on the door. The son was home on his own and was so scared of the strange appearance of the 'men' that he swiftly locked all the doors and refused to answer.

The stranger then suddenly appeared at the neighbour's place and asked questions about the family in a peculiar robot-like voice. He then returned to the 'car' and it went back up the drive towards the main road—and then suddenly vanished.

On other occasions, the whole herd of cows belonging to the farm would suddenly disappear and turn up immediately at a neighbour's farm down the road, or sometimes with a significant time displacement.

Several large silver discs were sighted flying or hovering over the farm area during the months of nerve-racking activity, and each time the flight paths seemed to be over the cliff edges and into the water close to Stack Rocks. One of these sightings had a strange twist to it.

On this occasion, the Coombs family was returning to the farm after an outing when they saw a large domed disc above their car. They were just a short distance from the farmhouse. The disc then ascended slightly and moved across the fields, about 200 feet up, towards the cliff edge then down over the water towards Stack Rocks, about a quarter-mile off the coast.

Shortly after they got home, the Coombs were so excited at the close encounter that they decided to go for a walk along the clifftop coast path to see if the disc was still in the vicinity. They walked some distance along the path until they had an unobstructed view of Stack Rocks. The outcrop is a very barren, small island of rugged rocks with no plant life of any kind. Even the sea birds seem to keep clear of them. The only things that seemed to be attracted to the rocks were the huge flying discs which disappeared when they approached close to the outcrop.

The family was looking for some minutes out towards the rocks when suddenly they sighted two humanlike figures moving around the base of the rock-face, close to the water. The activity went on for a short time. Then, to their great surprise, they saw what appeared to be a doorway opening and closing in the side of the rocks as the figures moved in and out. One of the figures stood momentarily in the doorway and stared across at them as they watched in astonishment.

Unnerved at this completely unexpected turn of events, the Coombs turned and ran back down the coast path to the farmhouse.

I am not aware of what events have taken place since the writing of the book, but the family did say on several occasions that they intended to leave the farm and move to another district. I wrote a letter to Mr and Mrs Coombs on 20th August 1993, but up to this time I have not received an answer. I wanted to let them know that I intended to carry out an investigation of the area by computer and that if anything showed up of particular interest I would include it in this book. I would still be very interested in establishing communication with them if they ever read this.

The first thing I did was to write to England and obtain a very accurate survey map of the immediate area. The positions of Ripperstone Farm and Stack Rocks, off the coast, were clearly shown. The homestead and farm buildings were clearly marked. It was quite easy to extract very accurate latitude and longitude positions in order to carry out a check by computer. For this I used the *Gridworks* program, produced by Rod Maupin and myself, which calculates very accurately harmonic geometric positions, track angles and distances.

The key position appeared to be close to Stack Rocks. The activity of the humanlike figures and the apparent opening in the side of the rock-face suggested the possibility of an underground base of some sort. Access for the flying discs could be under the water. Pure conjecture, of course, but there must be some reason for the craft regularly disappearing at this point.

The first thing to ascertain was if any harmonic associations were evident in the latitude position of the rock outcrop. This was a simple calculation and it did not take long to find a definite connection with the gravity values in the unified tables.

The latitude passing through the centre of the outcrop is:

Latitude 51° 46' 28.3872" north, or 51.774552° north.

The small-circle circumference at this latitude, in minutes of arc relative to the equator (nautical miles):

	= 13365.15919 minutes of arc
13365.15919 ÷ 6 ÷ 6	= 371.2544218 harmonic
Reciprocal	= 2.693570600 harmonic

The harmonic 26935706 is the value of 'E' (energy) in geometric terms if the reciprocal value of gravity (speed of light, 143791.36438 minutes of arc per grid second) is entered into harmonic Unified Equation 3. An excellent beginning to the mathematical investigation.

The next step was to see if a longitude position close to the small island backed this up. Again, a short series of calculations showed positive results.

The longitude which passes very close to the western end of the island is:

Longitude 5° 10' 35.3607744" west, or 5.176489104° west.

5.176489104 ÷ 6 ÷ 6   = 0.14379136438 harmonic

The harmonic of the gravity reciprocal in the unified tables, 143791.36438 minutes of arc per grid second.

We can now verify both these values in Unified Equation 3:

$$E = \sqrt{[(2c + \sqrt{1/c}) \times (2c)^2]}, \text{ where 'c'} = 143791.36438$$

$$\mathbf{26935706} = \sqrt{[(287582.7286 + \sqrt{1/287582.7286}) \times (287582.7286)^2]}$$

$$= \sqrt{(2875827286 + 5896829800)\ (82703825)} \text{ harmonics}$$

$$= \sqrt{(8772657086 \times 82703825)} \text{ harmonics}$$

$$= \sqrt{7255323} \text{ harmonics}$$

$$= \mathbf{26935706} \text{ harmonic}$$

The odds for these two interrelated harmonics being present at the Stack Rocks position by chance are so astronomical that there is no question that this particular geometric point has been chosen as an interdimensional gateway, for scientific reasons, by the operators of the unidentified flying discs. It is obvious that there is a strong association of light and gravity harmonics close in to the Stack Rocks formation. At this point, the discs could undergo a displacement in space-time and disappear from view.

I decided to use this position as a central point from which to check the coordinates connecting the key positions on Ripperstone Farm. The farmhouse and the outbuildings.

First, the farmhouse. The calculated latitude and longitude proved to be:

Latitude 51° 45' 22.977" north / Longitude 5° 09' 39.223" west

The distance from the Stack Rocks position to the farmhouse was equal to 74.06430786 seconds of arc (relative), with a harmonic association as follows:

74.06430786 ÷ 6 ÷ 6	= 2.057341885 harmonic
Multiplied by 2	= 4.114683770 harmonic
Squared	= 16.93062252 harmonic
Squared	= 286.6459789 harmonic
Divided by 2	= 143.3229894 harmonic

This is equal to the harmonic of 143322.99 minutes of arc per grid second which would be the actual speed of light at the latitude of the farmhouse, or the actual reciprocal harmonic of gravity at that point. (This can be calculated from the unified light and gravity tables.)

This was not all. The track angle from the rocks produced a further harmonic:

Track angle	= 152.0188042 degrees
360 - 152.0188042	= 207.9811958 degrees
207.9811958 x 6 x 6 x 6 x 6	= 26954363000 harmonic

The harmonic 26954363 is equivalent to the value 'E' in harmonic Unified Equation 3, if the value of 'c' is equal to 143891.36492 minutes of arc per grid second—the speed of light in a vacuum.

There is no doubt in my mind that the 'aliens', or whoever, project some type of electromagnetic signal from the Stack Rocks position and create certain manifestations at the farmhouse—possibly in the form of holograms. The manifestations would have appeared real to the Coombs family and certainly scared the daylights out of them.

The other position on the farm where unusual happenings occurred was around the milking sheds and other farm buildings. I carried out the same exercise and calculated the distance and track angle from the Stack Rocks point.

The position close to the farm buildings:

Latitude 51° 45' 33.912072" north / Longitude 5° 10' 02.5884" west

The distance from Stack Rocks	= 58.22855856 seconds of arc
	(relative)
58.22855856 ÷ 6 ÷ 6 ÷ 6	= 0.26957666 harmonic

The harmonic 26957666 is the value of 'E' (energy) in geometric terms if the value of 'c', 143909.0655 minutes of arc per grid second (electro-magnetic propagation speed) is entered into Harmonic Unified Equation 3.

Track angle	= 159.61248 degrees
159.61248 x 6 x 6 x 6 x 6 x 6 x 6 x 6 x 6 x 6 x 6 x 6 x 6	
	= 3.4744162^{11} harmonic
Multiplied by 2	= 6.9488325^{11} harmonic
Reciprocal	= 1.439090655^{-12} harmonic

The harmonic of 143909.0655 minutes of arc per grid second.

The latitude value of 51.75942002 degrees sets up another unusual association with the 143909.0655 harmonic. As mentioned earlier, the harmonic process can be related directly with linear, square or cubic measure based on multiple or divisional increments of 6—that is, 6, 36, 216.

In this case we are dealing with an area of a partial cross-section of the Earth. If we take a cross-sectional cut through the Earth's centre, then calculate the area of the pie-shaped segment between the equator and latitude 51.75942002 degrees (see Diagram 26), then we have the following:

Radius of the Earth in minute-of-arc values (nautical miles) relative to the Earth's surface: = 3437.74677 minutes of arc (naut. miles)

Therefore, area of the Earth's cross-section:

$$= 37127665.09 \text{ square minutes of arc}$$
$$\text{(nautical miles)}$$

$(37127665.09 \times 51.75942002) \div 360$

$$= 5338073.364 \text{ square minutes of arc}$$

$5338073.364 \div 36 \div 36$	$= 4118.883766$ harmonic
Squared	$= 16965203.47$ harmonic
Squared	$= 28781812^{14}$ harmonic
Divided by 2	$= 14390906^{14}$ harmonic

The harmonic of 143909.0655 minutes of arc per grid second.

This particular value becomes evident in many different areas of my research and appears to be related to the atomic structure of our reality. When this value of 'c' is entered into harmonic Unified Equation 2, it also shows a direct relationship with the Earth's magnetic fields. Could this be a key resonance for the manipulation of space-time?

The fact that this value is so prevalent in the geometric pattern of activity on Ripperstone Farm proves to me that the Coombs family was telling the truth about their frightening experiences.

It is difficult to figure out what the reason was for all the strange activities observed in this small area. Were the aliens purposely trying to scare the heck out of the Coombs family so that they could observe their reactions, or was some scientific experiment being carried out which just happened to be in the vicinity of the farm? We may never know the answer to this, but the Coombs family certainly had an exciting time for a few months.

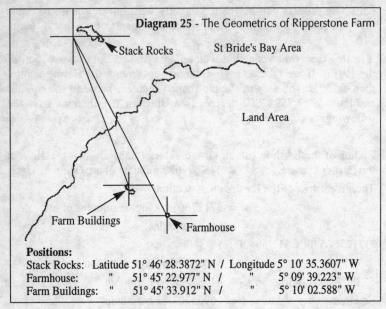

Diagram 25 - The Geometrics of Ripperstone Farm

St Bride's Bay Area

Stack Rocks

Land Area

Farm Buildings

Farmhouse

Positions:
Stack Rocks: Latitude 51° 46' 28.3872" N / Longitude 5° 10' 35.3607" W
Farmhouse: "   51° 45' 22.977" N /   "   5° 09' 39.223" W
Farm Buildings: "   51° 45' 33.912" N /   "   5° 10' 02.588" W

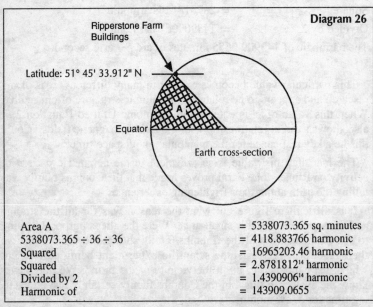

Diagram 26

Ripperstone Farm
Buildings

Latitude: 51° 45' 33.912" N

A

Equator

Earth cross-section

Area A	= 5338073.365 sq. minutes
5338073.365 ÷ 36 ÷ 36	= 4118.883766 harmonic
Squared	= 16965203.46 harmonic
Squared	= 2.8781812^{14} harmonic
Divided by 2	= 1.4390906^{14} harmonic
Harmonic of	= 143909.0655

Chapter Eighteen

THE *U.S.S. PUEBLO*

In January 1968, the North Koreans created an incident that could possibly have sparked off the start of World War III. They had the cheek to hijack one of America's electronic intelligence-gathering ships, said to be in international waters off the coast of Korea.

The *U.S.S. Pueblo* was a small, 179-foot-long, ship, fully equipped with the latest state-of-the-art intelligence-gathering gear: radars, sonars, navigation instruments and long-range radio. She was one of a fleet of ships that cruised the international waters off the coasts of China, North Korea and Russia. The Cold War was at its height and both Russia and America had similar ships that collected and analysed all communications between between the governments and military forces of the opposing factions.

The Captain of the *Pueblo*, Lloyd M. Bucher, was not particularly worried when a North Korean torpedo boat approached the *Pueblo*. Both sides were quite used to being harassed by their counterparts during the game of electronic snooping. The situation rapidly changed, though, about an hour later when three more North Korean ships appeared and took up station around his boat.

Bucher had no choice other than to follow orders signalled to him and allow his boat to be herded into the port of Wonsan. Before shutting down transmission, the *Pueblo* radioed a message to Yokosuka that they had been boarded by North Koreans and the ship was under arrest.

Then all hell broke loose. The Americans were naturally upset about the pirate action and considered the incident an "act of war". Threats were made, but eventually things calmed down a little and the American authorities backed off any direct confrontation. The crew was released and returned to the United States.

At the time, the story was world news and everybody had bated breath wondering what the outcome would be. Any reader who wishes to know more about the incident will find plenty of information in the newspaper archives of the time.

What interested me was why the Koreans had zeroed in on this particular boat. Was it, in fact, within the 12-mile limit and in territorial waters as they claimed? Was there something special about the action that made the Koreans and possibly the Russians edgy?

The Americans said the ship was in international waters at latitude 39° 25' north and longitude 127° 54' east. The North Koreans insisted that the ship was in their territorial waters at latitude 39° 17' north and longitude 127° 47' east.

Out of curiosity I decided to check the position closer inland to see if there was anything unusual about it that would alert the Koreans. The Russian naval base at Vladivostok was not too far north and the Chinese atomic testing ground at Lop Nor was inland to the north-west.

The position of the *Pueblo* claimed by the Koreans was given in degrees and minutes of arc. A more accurate position would have been given in degrees, minutes and seconds, each second being equivalent to 100 geodetic feet.

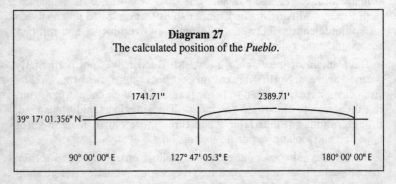

Diagram 27
The calculated position of the *Pueblo*.

I found that by adding the small increments of 1.356 seconds to the latitude and 5.3 seconds to the longitude values, the following harmonics would be evident:

Great-circle distance to 180°	= 2389.71 minutes
Great-circle distance to 90°	= <u>1741.71</u> minutes
Difference (relative)	= <u>648.00</u> minutes
Square root of 648	= 25.455844 harmonic

| Reciprocal | = 0.03928371 harmonic |
| The *Pueblo* latitude | = 39.28371 degrees |

It can be seen that both the latitude and the longitude of the ship position would set up a harmonic related to the Earth's magnetic fields, 3928371.

The odds that such a small correction would produce the harmonic values associated with the unified tables would give credence to the fact that the Koreans did not specify this position randomly. It is almost certain that at some time the American ship had occupied this location and that for some reason it was important enough for the ship to breach the 12 mile territorial limit.

The actual speed-of-light values for this latitude also reinforced the circumstantial evidence that the ship was, at one time, stationed at this position.

The actual speed of light (gravity reciprocal) calculated from the geometric unified tables for this latitude:	= 143486.5739 ±1
144000 - 143486.5739	= 513.42612 harmonic
Squared	= 263606.3806 harmonic

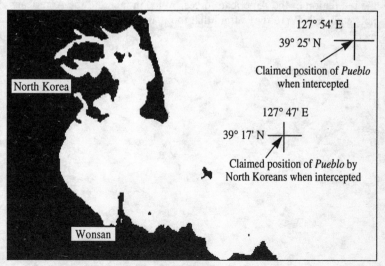

Map 2 - Showing the claimed positions of *Pueblo* when intercepted.

Squared $= 6.9488323$ harmonic

Reciprocal $= 1.43909065^{-11}$ harmonic

The harmonic of 143909.0655 minutes of arc per grid second.

The actual speed of light (vacuum) calculated from the geometric unified tables for this latitude: $= 143586.2845 \pm 1$

144000 - 143586.2845 $= 413.71554$ harmonic

$413.71554 \times 6 \times 6 \times 6 \times 6 \times 6 \times 6 \times 6 \times 6$ $= 69488325$ harmonic

Reciprocal $= 1.439090655^{-9}$ harmonic

The harmonic of 143909.0655 minutes of arc per grid second.

I have found that this 143909.0655 value becomes evident quite frequently in my investigations of scientific activity around the world, particularly in communications. The fact that the *Pueblo* was in a perfect position to intercept transmissions from the Russian Naval base at Vladivostok and from the Chinese atomic test grounds at Lop Nor probably triggered the hostile action.

Whatever roused the anger of the Koreans (possibly encouraged by the Russians and Chinese), it must have been important enough to risk the retaliation of the American forces. Why, in fact, did the Americans not retaliate? Were they afraid that too many secrets would be uncovered?

Chapter Nineteen

THE CATASTROPHE AT KYSHTYM

How many of us in the Western world have heard of a town called Kyshtym? It is, or was, situated close to the Ural mountain range in the former Soviet Union, and until one fatal day in late 1957 it was a thriving community of around 150,000 people in one of the most populated areas of the country. Today there could be less than 50,000 of these people alive and they can only look forward to a questionable future because of a possible slow and painful death by radiation poisoning.

It is said that the town was once a thriving industrial centre, but now marks the ground zero point of a few thousand square kilometres of barren wasteland and death. The area is scattered with the remains of forests and farmland, the rubble of houses and deserted villages. Not a thing moves; no animals, birds or a single human being can be seen. The lucky ones died instantly when a gigantic explosion razed the countryside. Many more died months later from radiation poisoning and the rest are succumbing slowly to the effects of leukaemia and other types of cancers.

The story has been suppressed by the Soviets and the scientists of the West for many years and it is only in recent times that the facts were made known by a Russian scientist who is now living in London. He spent two years investigating the incident to try to find the truth. This was the biggest nuclear disaster since the bombing of Hiroshima and Nagasaki and the authorities were desperate to keep the story from the world.

When the scientist Zhores Medvedev arrived in the West in 1973, he was surprised that word of the incident had not leaked out. He said that "most Russian scientists had at least indirect knowledge of the disaster" and added that he had known about it for years. It is said that the horrendous explosion was caused by the accidental detonation of high-quality nuclear waste from one of the Russians' weapons projects that had been buried in trenches in the vicinity of the town.

When Medvedev mentioned the incident in a magazine article which he was asked to write regarding the scientific achievements of the Russians, there was an immediate reaction from the Western press. Round about this time there was much argument going on about the disposal of nuclear waste that was being shipped to England from Japan and no one wanted any rocking of the boat by news of this nature. The Soviets, as usual, said nothing, but the nuclear experts from France, Britain and the United States pronounced the whole story as rubbish. Medvedev was most disturbed at the violent reaction by the Western scientists to his article.

"They were putting my reputation in question. I was represented as an anti-nuclear activist and they made out that I wanted people to be afraid of nuclear power. That was not true, so I had to make some effort to clear myself and to prove that I was not writing science fiction."

In order to present all the known facts, he wrote a book called *Nuclear Disaster in the Urals*, and this effectively silenced the critics.

More information to back up the story came from Professor Lev Tumerman, who is now the head of the physics department of the Jerusalem University. He left his native land and migrated to Israel in the early '70s. He has actually travelled through the disaster area, and described the scene as follows:

"The signs warned the drivers not to stop for the next 30 kilometres and to drive through at maximum speed and with all the windows shut. On both sides of the road, as far as the eye could see, the land was dead and no villages or towns existed. Only the chimneys of the destroyed houses.

"There were no cultivated fields, no herds, no people, nothing. The whole area was exceedingly hot. An enormous area had been laid waste, rendered useless and unproductive for a very long time, perhaps for hundreds of years. When the Americans had their emergency at Three Mile Island nuclear power station, the Soviet authorities gloated that no such emergency had ever happened in Russia. They said their safeguards were so thorough that every possible emergency could be dealt with. Of course they were lying. They had not only an emergency, but a disaster."

When I read the story a couple of years ago I was highly intrigued, and clipped it out of the newspaper for filing and future reference as there was a mass of evidence now available that proved conclusively that an atomic explosion could only be caused by a geometric process. (I have demonstrated this in my previous books.) This has also been admitted to me by intelligence personnel and a nuclear scientist. The Russians, of course, would be fully aware of this through their own nuclear programs.

I would not have thought that atomic waste, no matter how carelessly disposed of, could have caused such a gigantic explosion. The geometric arrangements necessary for the detonation of an atomic bomb are very complex and require an exact process, so it seems unlikely that, without some unknown factor being present in the area, an explosion could occur. But facts are facts and, regardless of the reason, the catastrophe did take place. The truth of the matter may never be known.

Obviously all the required geometric coordinates were present at the point of detonation, so a computer check of the area should show the probability of an explosion if certain harmonic values were evident.

The central position of the town of Kyshtym, according to my volume of the *Times World Index*, is:

Latitude 55° 43' north / Longitude 60° 32' east

The calculated latitude and longitude associated with grid harmonics:

Latitude 55° 42' 54.958" north / Longitude 60° 32' 31.844472" east

The actual speed of light (gravitational acceleration reciprocal), calculated from the geometric unified tables for this latitude, is 143273.2843 ±1 minutes of arc per grid second. If we subtract this from the maximum we get:

144000 - 143273.2843	= 726.71575 harmonic
Square root	= 26.957666 harmonic

This is the harmonic of 'E' (energy), 26957666, if the value 143909.0655 minutes of arc per grid second is entered into Harmonic Unified Equation 3.

The actual speed of light (vacuum) calculated from the geometric unified tables for this latitude is 143373.185 ±1. If we subtract this from the maximum, we get:

144000 - 143373.185	= 626.815 harmonic

$626.815 \div 6 \div 6 \div 6 \div 6$	$= 0.483653548$ harmonic
Square root	$= 0.69545205$ harmonic
Reciprocal	$= 1.4379136$ harmonic

The harmonic of 143791.36 minutes of arc per grid second (gravity reciprocal).

The difference in longitude from longitude zero and longitude 90 degrees of the harmonic point is equal to:

$60.54217902 - 29.45782098$	$= 31.08435804$ harmonic
$31.08435804 \div 6 \div 6 \div 6$	$= 0.1439090655$ harmonic

The harmonic of 143909.0655 minutes of arc per grid second. (See Diagram 29.) The harmonic factor of 143909.0655 can also be found in the pie-shaped cross-sectional area between the equator and the latitude at Kyshtym. (See Diagram 28.)

The geometric evidence indicates that Kyshtym was not a randomly chosen position for atomic experimentation. The geometric coordinates centred on this area made it a most probable position for an atomic detonation if all the right parameters were brought together at the right instant of time.

The harmonics associated with gravitation and the unified field were, without doubt, the prime cause of the explosion and consequent devastation. I do not believe that an atomic waste dump was the only cause. Could this have been an experiment that went radically wrong? Did the scientists overreach themselves in their search for knowledge?

The geometric harmonic of this value can be shifted up or down the scale by multiplying or dividing by (6 x 6) or 36. So:

$5746049.321 \times 36 \times 36 \times 36 \times 36 \times 36$	
	$= 3.4744162^{14}$ harmonic
Multiplied by 2	$= 6.9488325^{14}$ harmonic
Reciprocal	$= 1.439090655^{-15}$ harmonic
	$= \mathbf{143909.0655}$ harmonic

The speed of light (electromagnetic). (See gravity conversion tables.)

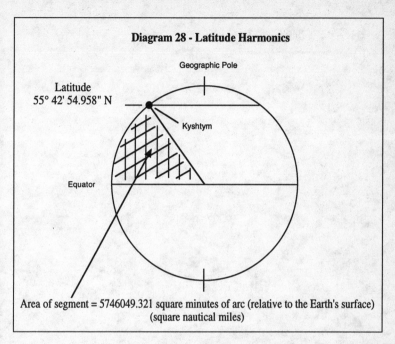

Diagram 28 - Latitude Harmonics

Geographic Pole

Latitude
55° 42' 54.958" N

Kyshtym

Equator

Area of segment = 5746049.321 square minutes of arc (relative to the Earth's surface)
(square nautical miles)

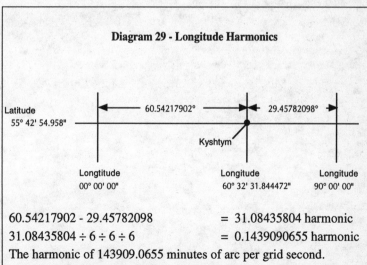

Diagram 29 - Longitude Harmonics

Latitude
55° 42' 54.958"

60.54217902° ⟶ ⟵ 29.45782098°

Kyshtym

Longtitude
00° 00' 00"

Longitude
60° 32' 31.844472"

Longitude
90° 00' 00"

60.54217902 - 29.45782098 = 31.08435804 harmonic
31.08435804 ÷ 6 ÷ 6 ÷ 6 = 0.1439090655 harmonic
The harmonic of 143909.0655 minutes of arc per grid second.

Chapter Twenty

THE HARMONICS OF A BLACK HOLE

The harmonic unified tables indicate to us that the Universe is manifested from the gravitational fields. The whole of our reality and sense of time is created by the interlocking electromagnetic wave-forms which come into being due to an inverse reaction to the all-pervading gravitational forces. We live in a type of galactic hologram that appears to us to have form and solidity, but in fact can be likened to nothing more than a puff of smoke. The Grand Illusion.

The tables also tell us that as the gravitational force increases, the 'speed' or acceleration of light, or electromagnetic propagation, decreases. The tables, therefore, help to explain black holes.

Black holes are regions in space where the gravitational forces have increased to such an extent that no atomic particles can escape, even at the speed of light. The perfect atomic prison. They are formed when a star of certain mass limits, consumes all of its thermonuclear energy and collapses to a fraction of its normal size. The surface of the mass then becomes a gravitational boundary which is called the event horizon.

In the case of a non-rotating black hole, the collapsed matter is crushed to theoretical zero volume and infinite density at what is called the singularity, or centre.

In the case of a rotating black hole, this state of oblivion or singularity need not occur. It has been suggested that this type may provide a gateway to another Universe or, possibly, anti-Universe.

The radius of a black hole is proportional to its mass. The density of a black hole at the time of formation is inversely proportional to the square of its mass.

According to theory, the radius of the Earth would have to be reduced to nearly a third of an inch in order to create a black hole, which brings us to an extremely interesting proposition.

I assumed that if the unified tables that I had calculated were correct, then the geometry in relation to the event horizon of a black hole would have to conform to the unified values. If a relationship could be found, then the geometry of all black holes would follow a similar pattern.

A short time on the computer indicated that the critical radius for the formation of a black hole from an Earth-size planet would be:

$$= 0.33371977 \text{ British inches}$$
$$= 0.32954553 \text{ geodetic inches}$$

The radius of the Earth:

$$= 3437.74677 \text{ nautical miles}$$
(minutes of arc)
$$= 20626480.62 \text{ geodetic feet}$$
$$= 247517767.4 \text{ geodetic inches}$$

Therefore, the radius of the Earth divided by the radius of the theoretical black hole is:

247517767.4 ÷ 0.3295455   = 751088225.6 units.

If we shift this value on the harmonic scale by the division of 6, then:

751088225.6 ÷ 6 ÷ 6   = 20863561.81 harmonic

If we now check the unified tables, we find that the similar harmonic of 208.635618 is the difference between the light harmonic, which is the reciprocal of gravity acceleration, and the maximum of 144000.

The value 208.635618 is also three times the gravity acceleration harmonic of 69.5452056, which in turn is the reciprocal of the harmonic 143791.36, the acceleration of light at that level.

A bit confusing, but a study of the tables will show the relationships.

This will demonstrate that the radius of a black hole has a very definite relationship with the gravity acceleration value at the equator of the original body before collapse.

The circumference of the black hole, which forms the event horizon, also conforms to the unified geometric values.

A black hole radius of:	0.32954553 geodetic inches
	= 0.027462127 geodetic feet
Therefore, diameter	= 0.054924255 geodetic feet
Therefore, circumference	= 0.172549636 geodetic feet
	= 2.8758272^{-5} nautical miles
Divided by 2	= 1.4379136^{-5} harmonic

Again, this is the harmonic of 143791.36 minutes of arc per grid second, or the gravitational reciprocal.

A rotating black hole is said to give off some radiation due to the spin. This should be so if the circumference at the event horizon is harmonically tuned to the gravitational speed-of-light value. Each revolution would create a wave in resonance with the reciprocal light factor of the gravity forces.

I note in Stephen Hawking's book, *Beyond the Black Hole*, he states:

"Although particle physicists may be coming close to a unified theory of the Universe with the three forces that push and pull within the atom, gravitation is still the odd force out."

And also:

"There are several groups of scientists working on unifying all the forces, trying to add gravity to the other three. Gell-Mann told me, 'Most of them don't know what they are doing. They're just using various mathematical tricks.'"

I would respectfully suggest that they approach the problem by the use of unified geometry.

Time will tell whether this approach is correct.

Chapter Twenty-One

HARMONIC CLUES TO THE UNIFIED FIELDS

The Harmonics of the Soviet Ratan-600 Radio Telescope

This device, built to probe the galaxy, includes a large circular mirror which has a given diameter of 1,890 feet. This is made up of 895 separate moveable panels, each 6.6 by 24 feet. Inside the circle is a moveable plane mirror 1,312 feet long and 27 feet high, plus five focal receiving stations mounted on rails. Each one contains a secondary reflector of 26 by 18 feet. It operates within a range of 8 millimetres and 20 centimetres wavelength.

The position of the telescope is given as close to the town of Zelenchukskaya in the Caucasus mountains.

A routine check of the given diameter of this gigantic instrument again showed a correlation with the secret unified geometry.

Diameter 1,890 feet divided by 6,076   = 0.311059907 n. miles

Therefore, circumference of circle   = 0.977223521 n. miles

One nautical mile is equal to one minute of arc.

A shift in the harmonic scale by the powers of 6:

$0.977223521 \div 6 \div 6 \div 6 \div 6 \div 6 \div 6 \div 6 \div 6 \div 6 \div 6$

$$= 2.6935817^{-9} \text{ harmonic}$$

This is very close to the value of 'E' in Unified Equation 3 when the gravity reciprocal value of 143791.36438 is inserted into the equation—the 26935706 harmonic.

Therefore, working backwards:

2.6935706^{-9} x 6 x 6 x 6 x 6 x 6 x 6 x 6 x 6 x 6 x 6 x 6

$$= 0.97721948 \text{ n.m. circumference}$$
$$= 0.31105862 \text{ naut.miles diameter}$$
$$= 1889.99210 \text{ feet}$$

The fractional error is so small that I feel certain the instrument has been tuned to gravitational harmonics.

The Great Pyramid Harmonics

In my earlier books I demonstrated how the geometric unified harmonics were incorporated in the construction of the Great Pyramid in Egypt:

"It is obvious that knowledge of vast importance to mankind is locked up in the secrets of the pyramids, and the very word pyramid *should give us the first clue. The literal meaning is "fire in the middle". On page 86 of* The Great Pyramid—Its Divine Message, *by D Davidson and H. Aldersmith, another derivation of the word is given.* Pyramid *is the Grecianised form of the Hebrew* Urrim-Middin *("light measures"). The Egyptian name for the Great Pyramid is* Khuti *("the lights"). In the Semitic languages, the equivalent name is* Urim *("the lights"). In Chaldee and Hebrew,* Middin *means "treasures", hence the Chaldee-Hebrew name of the Great Pyramid. In Egyptian,* Khuti *("the lights") is* Urim-Middin *(Purim-Middin or "lights-measures").*

"The geometric analysis of the Great Pyramid made it evident that the light and gravity harmonics were incorporated throughout the structure. The purpose of the completed stone complex is yet to be discovered but I still believe that one of the main functions was communication over vast distances."

Now that *Gridworks*, the computer program for calculating the world energy grid system, is available it is possible to demonstrate that the geometric positioning of the Pyramid was also an important factor governing the harmonic tuning to the light and gravity resonances.

The position of the Pyramid is generally given as:

Latitude 29° 58' 51" north / Longitude 31° 09' 00" east

The latitude value can be taken as fairly accurate but, as yet, I have been unable to obtain a modern, accurate, large-scale survey map of the area that shows the true longitude clearly.

I have found that if I use a position of:

Latitude 29° 58' 50.952" north / Longitude 139° 09' 35.52" east,
the computer will produce a position on Grid "B" (the world energy grid system) of:

Latitude 21° 21' 14.573" north / Longitude 139° 53' 09.95" east, or
Latitude 21.3540482° north / Longitude 139.8860974° east

If we examine the latitude value harmonically within the 90° sector, we have:

90 - 21.3540482	= 68.6459518
Multiplied by the 6 harmonic	= 411.8757108
Squared	= 169641.604
Squared	= 2.87782720^{10}
Divided by 2	= 1.43891360^{10} harmonic

This is the harmonic of the speed of light in a vacuum, 143891.36 minutes of arc per grid second.

Examining the longitude value harmonically:

139.8860974 - 90	= 49.8860974
90 - 49.8860974	= 40.1139026
49.8860974 - 40.1139026	= 9.77219480 harmonic

Harmonic shift divided by 6:

9.7721948 ÷6÷6÷6÷6÷6÷6÷6÷6÷6÷6÷6 = 2.6935706^{-8} harmonic

Harmonic 26935706 is equal to the value of 'E' in harmonic Unified Equation 3 when the gravitational reciprocal value 143791.36 is entered into the equation.

More research is yet to be carried out on this as more information becomes available, and further fractional corrections are made to the computer programs, but the calculations so far are showing some interesting results.

It appears that the Great Pyramid is placed very accurately on the world energy grid system.

Experiments by Dr T. Henry Moray

Dr Hans A. Nieper writes in one of his books:

"The American physicist Dr T. Henry Moray directed Tesla-modulated frequencies into a 15-metre insulated cable. By this he was able to extract up to 70 kW of useful electrical energy."

This was in the late '20s and early '30s. These were experiments to extract energy directly from the surrounding gravitational fields.

If we want to convert metres into harmonic units, then:

$(15 \times 39.370079 \times 6000) \div (12 \times 6076)$ $\quad = 48.59703629$

$48.59703629 \div 6 \div 6 \div 6 \div 6 \div 6 \div 6 \div 6 \div 6 \div 6 \quad = 4.8222367^{-6}$ harmonic

Square root of the 48.222367 harmonic $\quad = 6.9442326^{-3}$ harmonic

It appears that a length very close to 15 metres produces the harmonic reciprocal of the maximum light speed, 144000 minutes of arc per grid second, namely, 6944444. Tesla and Moray knew how to tune their circuits.

The Harmonics of the Area of the Sun's Cross-Section in Relation to the Earth

Radius of the Sun is given as $\quad = 696,000$ kilometres

Conversion to nautical miles, or minutes of arc relative to the Earth's surface:

$(696000 \times 3280.839) \div 6076 \quad = 375816.9756$ n. miles

Therefore, area of the Sun's cross-section $\quad = 4.4371351^{11}$ sq. n. miles

Shifting harmonically:

$4.4371351^{11} \times 36 \times 36 \times 36 \times 36 \times 36 \times 36 \times 36 \quad = 3.4771238^{22}$ harmonic

Multiplied by 2 $\quad = 6.9542477^{22}$ harmonic

If we use the gravity acceleration value of 695452056 harmonic at the Earth's surface, derived from the unified tables, and work backwards, we have:

$6.95452056^{22} \div 2 \quad = 3.47726028^{22}$

$3.47726028^{22} \div 36 \div 36 \div 36 \div 36 \div 36 \div 36 \quad = 4.4373092^{11}$ sq. n. miles

Therefore, the radius $\quad = 375824.34$ naut. miles

$\quad = 696013.6495$ km

The difference of 13.6495 km is so small that I would venture to say that the area of the Sun's cross-section is harmonically tuned to the value of gravity acceleration at the Earth's surface.

The Harmonics of the Earth's Orbit

It was recently brought to my attention that the Earth's orbit has a definite harmonic association with the geometry of the unified fields. Mr Jeffrey Cook of Derbyshire, England, has sent me many small snippets of information over the years, and in his latest letter he says:

"I am still convinced that the elliptical orbit of the Earth and its varying distance from the Sun contains all the important harmonic values you have discovered, when the distances are expressed in nautical miles." (minutes of arc at the Earth's surface).

According to the astronomy books, the Earth lies at an average distance of 93 million miles from the Sun. It can come as close as 91.4 million miles, perihelion, or as far as 94.5 million miles, aphelion.

Average value, 93 million miles	= 80,816,326.53 nautical miles
Therefore, radius of orbit	= 80,816,326.53 nautical miles
Diameter of orbit	= 161,632,653 nautical miles
161,632,653 ÷ 60	= 2,693,877.55 degrees (relative)

It appears that the average diameter of the Earth's orbit could have a direct association with the energy harmonic derived from Unified Equation 3 when the gravity reciprocal value 143791.36 is entered into the equation, or:

E	= 26935706 harmonic

Working backwards:

2,693,570.6 x 60	= 161,614,242 n. miles diameter
Divided by 2	= 80,807,118 naut. miles radius
	= 92,989,403.2 miles av. radius

A very close check of the absolute values of orbital distance should indicate some surprising correlations with the unified tables.

The Earth-Sun relationship could be the key to the unlocking of all the harmonic geometrics of the solar system and help to prove the unified concepts. This alone will be a very interesting study for the future. Thank you, Jeffrey.

The Harmonic Cross-Sectional Area of the Earth in Relation to Gravitation

The circumference of the Earth is equal to 21,600 nautical miles, or minutes of arc at the Earth's surface. The radius is therefore 3437.74677 nautical miles, or minutes of arc (relative).

From this we can calculate the area of the Earth's cross-section in square nautical miles, or minutes of arc (relative).

3437.74677 x 3437.74677 x 3.1415926

	= 37127665.09 sq. nautical miles
Reciprocal	= 26934093 harmonic
	(disregarding decimal points)

The harmonic 26934093 is very close to the value 'E' in Unified Equation 3 if the gravity reciprocal value of 143791.2143565 minutes of arc per grid second is the 'c' value entered into the equation. The value for 'E' would then be harmonic 26935678.

As all matter is manifested from the unified fields of space, it is possible that the geometry of the Earth's cross-section is arranged in such a way that this particular gravitational value becomes evident.

I discovered by calculation that a very accurate geometric pattern could be achieved if it was assumed that the Earth had a comparatively small inner core of plasma.

The radius of the core would be 26.371438 nautical miles, or minutes of arc relative to the Earth's surface.

| Square of 26.371438 | = 695.45278 harmonic |
| Reciprocal | = 1.437912143565^{-3} |

The harmonic 143791.2143565 is the reciprocal of the gravitational acceleration value in the electromagnetic propagation unified tables.

The area of the cross-section of the inner plasma core would be:

= 2184.829225 square naut. miles

If we now subtract the cross-sectional area of the plasma core from the total cross-sectional area of the Earth, then:

37127665.09 - 2184.829225 = 37125480.27

Reciprocal   = **26935678** harmonic
                                              (disregarding decimal points)

The value for 'E' in Unified Equation 3 is as follows, where 'c' is equal to 143791.2143565:

$E = \sqrt{[(2c + \sqrt{1/2c}) \times (2c)^2]}$

$= \sqrt{[(287582.4286 + \sqrt{1/287582.4286}) \times (287582.4286)^2]}$

$= \sqrt{[(287582.4286 + 5896832972)(8270365324)]}$ harmonics

$= \sqrt{(8772657258 \times 8270365324)}$ harmonics

$= \sqrt{7255308}$ harmonics

= **26935678** harmonic (disregarding decimal points).

The Harmonic Cross-Sectional Area of the Earth in Relation to Gravitation

Radius of the Earth   = 3437.74677 naut. miles (mins. of arc)

Circumference of the Earth   = 21,600 nautical miles (minutes of arc)

Total area of cross-section   = 37127665.09 square nautical miles

The harmonic of gravity acceleration at the Earth's surface (equator) is equal to 6.954527816^{-5}.

The harmonic reciprocal (speed of light) is equal to 143791.2143565 minutes of arc per grid second (electromagnetic table).

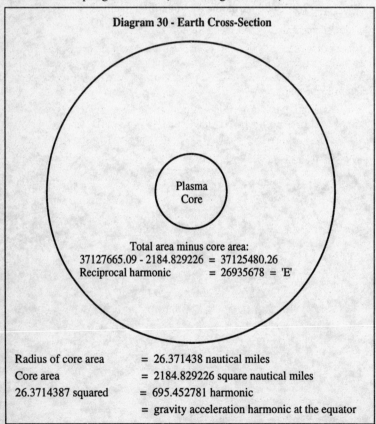

Diagram 30 - Earth Cross-Section

Plasma Core

Total area minus core area:
37127665.09 - 2184.829226 = 37125480.26
Reciprocal harmonic   = 26935678 = 'E'

Radius of core area   = 26.371438 nautical miles

Core area   = 2184.829226 square nautical miles

26.3714387 squared   = 695.452781 harmonic

                          = gravity acceleration harmonic at the equator

Epilogue

This book has been written mainly for the serious researcher who wishes to delve into the secrets of the harmonic structure of the Universe. I realise that the information enclosed is only a first faltering step into the concepts of harmonic mathematics, but I am quietly confident that the values demonstrated are reasonably accurate and that many scientific projects are in progress in various countries around the world that make use of this hidden knowledge.

I have discovered a number of structures myself that conform to the harmonic concepts. The geometric positioning and relationship with other sites sometimes suggests that other, more secret activity is taking place in certain areas.

All of this unpublished information I have filed and lodged in safe keeping, and I have also forwarded copies to higher authorities.

Certain transmitters and power stations fall into this category. Some of the interesting harmonics evident are displacements of 509.11688 minutes of arc and 208.635617 degrees between installations, and various latitudes and longitudes that give specific harmonic resonances— one value being latitude 41.188837 degrees. The clues to the harmonic relationships are to be found in the demonstrated unified tables and unified equations. The unified equations have been tested and found to be correct.

Billions of dollars are being spent on this activity—and it's our money. We have a right to know who is controlling the secret projects and what the final outcome is going to be.

I have stated before in my writings that we are being conned, and the present uncovered evidence more than reinforces this statement. In the past, thousands of my books were destroyed without explanation, and my work was virtually forced off the market. I was informed by an intelligence agent some years ago that my work would be suppressed, and "they", whoever they are, have almost succeeded.

Almost—but not quite.

INDEX

GRIDWORKS

THE WORLD ENERGY GRID PROGRAM

The program calculates with extreme accuracy:

Minimum Requirements
- IBM compatible PC
- 640K, 1MB hard disk
- Mono or CGA (no graphics)
- EGA or VGA (for graphics)

- Great circle tracks and distances.
- Light and gravity harmonics for any latitude.
- Earth coordinate (latitude and longitude) to Energy Grid coordinate conversion.
- Energy Grid to Earth coordinate conversion.
- Calculation of Grid A and Grid B points over any section of the world.
- If your computer has graphics capabilities, Gridworks will draw a map of the world and overlay a calculated grid over it.
- Conversion values for miles, nautical miles, kilometres, etc.
- Will also print out the complete gravity and light table.

"This computer program is the culmination of 27 years of extensive research into the UFO enigma, by myself, and over two years of close cooperation with computer expert Rodney Maupin of Seattle, Washington, USA.

Over the years I have been asked hundreds of times by members of the public whether I could supply maps or information regarding the Grid network for particular areas of the Earth's surface. I could only reply that it was impossible for me to calculate sections of the Grid for other parts of the world because of the spherical geometry involved. The problem could only be tackled with the help of a computer, and then only if specialised programs were available. It is only in recent years that this has become possible. I was visited by Rod Maupin just over two years ago and it turned out that he was the only one who understood my work and had the necessary programming skills to create the World Grid program. This work is the result—the first of its type in the world made available to the public."

Captain Bruce L. Cathie (Ret.)

To order: Send US$175.00 cheque/bank draft/credit card, payable to NEXUS Magazine
(This price includes postage & packing to any part of the world)

NEXUS Magazine, PO Box 30, Mapleton Qld 4560 Australia.

(NB: Please indicate disk size - 5.25" DS:DD, 5.25" DS:HD, 3.5" DS:HD, 3.5" DS:DD etc.)

BRUCE CATHIE VIDEOS

Two videos of presentations given by Bruce Cathie are available through NEXUS Magazine.

1) SECRET TECHNOLOGY & THE WORLD ENERGY SYSTEM

112 minutes, PAL-VHS — AUD$45.00 (includes p&h in Australia)
— AUD$50.00 (airmail to NZ)

In this rare account, Capt. Bruce Cathie (Ret.) of New Zealand tells his personal story. From 27 years of research to prove the Unified Field Theory, Bruce goes on to prove the existence of the World Energy Grid system—its use and misuse, and the reasons that it has been kept secret. Topics include: Harmonic Geometries of Reality, Atom Bomb Cover-up, Power Stations, Ground Aerials, The Moon-Mars-Pyramid Harmonics, Space Transmitters, Crop Circles, Anti-Gravity, The Great Pyramid, The Philadelphia Experiment, UFOs, The Human Body, and more.

2) BRUCE CATHIE IN CONFERENCE VIDEO

180 minutes, PAL-VHS — AUD$50.00 (includes p&p in Australia)
— AUD$55.00 (airmail to NZ)

In May of 1992, a conference was held in Sydney and Brisbane, Australia. The two speakers at these conferences were Bruce Cathie and Stan Deyo. The best of Bruce's slide presentation is captured on this 3 hour video. Topics include: Harmonic Geometries of Reality, Atom Bomb Cover-up, Power Stations, Ground Aerials, The Moon-Mars-Pyramid Harmonics, Space Transmitters, Crop Circles, Anti-Gravity, The Great Pyramid, The Philadelphia Experiment, UFOs, The Human Body, and more.
The video comes with a printed table of anti-gravity values.

Send to: NEXUS Magazine (Master/Visa Card accepted)
PO Box 30, Mapleton Qld 4560
Tel: 074 429 280 (International - +61 74 429 280)
Fax: 074 429 381 (International - +61 74 429 381)

NEXUS MAGAZINE

NEXUS Magazine is an Australian-based publication produced every two months. It covers unusual and hard-to-get information on the topics of health, science, the unexplained, and world events. NEXUS is currently read by over 120,000 people throughout Australia, New Zealand, USA, Canada, UK and The Netherlands.

Subscription details:

Australia •	AUD$25.00 (1 year) sample copy AUD$5.00	AUD$45.00 (2 years)
NZ, PNG •	AUD$40.00 (1 year) sample copy AUD$6.50	AUD$75.00 (2 years)
SE Asia •	AUD$45.00 (1 year) sample copy AUD$7.00	AUD$85.00 (2 years)
USA ••	USD$25.00 (1 year) sample copy USD$5.00	USD$45.00 (2 years)
Canada ••	USD$30.00 (1 year) sample copy USD$6.00	USD$55.00 (2 years)
UK •••	STG£18.00 (1 year) sample copy STG£3.00	STG£35.00 (2 years)
Netherlands ••••	NFLf50.00 (1 year) sample copy NFLf9.00	NFLf95.00 (2 years)
Europe ••••	NFLf60.00 (1 year) sample copy NFLf10.00	NFLf115.00 (2 years)

- • = Send to Australian (Head) Office. (Master/Visa Card accepted)
  PO Box 30, Mapleton Qld 4560
  Tel: 074 429 280 (International - +61 74 429 280)
  Fax: 074 429 381 (International - +61 74 429 381)

- •• = Send to USA Office (Master/Visa Card accepted)
  PO Box 177, Kempton IL 60946-0177
  Tel: 815 253 6464; Fax: 815 253 6300

- ••• = Send to UK Office (Master/Visa Card accepted)
  55 Queens Rd., E. Grinstead, W. Sussex RH19 1BG
  Tel: 0342 322854; Fax: 0342 324574

- •••• = Send to Netherlands Office (Master/Visa Card accepted)
  PO Box 372, 8250 AJ Dronten
  Tel: 3210 18892; Fax: 3210 18562